Free Stuff

FOR

Stitchers

ON THE

INTERNET

Judy Heim and Gloria Hansen

Copyright © 1999 Judy Heim and Gloria Hansen
Developmental Editor: Barbara Konzak Kuhn
Technical Editor: Beate Nellemann
Cover Design: Christina Jarumay
Book Design: Christina Jarumay
Book Production: Nancy Koerner
Front Cover Illustration: Alan McCorkle and Christina Jarumay

The copyrights on individual web sites/works are retained by the owners as noted. All rights reserved. No part of this work covered by the copyright hereon may be reproduced or used in any form or by any means—graphic, electronic, or mechanical, including photocopying, recording, taping, or information storage and retrieval systems—without written permission of the publisher.

We take great care to ensure that the information included in this book is accurate and presented in good faith, but no warranty is provided nor results guaranteed. Since we have no control over the choice of materials or procedure used, neither the authors nor C&T Publishing, Inc. shall have any liability to any person or entity with respect to any loss or damage caused directly or indirectly by the information contained in this book.

Library of Congress Cataloging-in-Publication Data
Heim, Judy.
    Free stuff for stitchers on the Internet / Judy Heim & Gloria Hansen.
    p. cm.
  Includes index.
  ISBN 1-57120-067-3 (pbk.)
    1. Needlework--Computer network resources--Directories.
  2. Internet (Computer network)--Directories. 3. Web sites--Directories.
  4. Free material--Directories. I. Hansen, Gloria. II. Title
    TT751 .H44 1999
    025.06'746--dc21
                                                        99-6155
                                                          CIP

Trademarked (™) and Registered Trademarked (®) names are used throughout this book. Rather than use the symbols with every occurrence of a trademark and registered trademark name, we are using the names only in an editorial fashion and to the benefit of the owner, with no intention of infringement.

Published by C&T Publishing, Inc.
P.O. Box 1456
Lafayette, California 94549

Printed in Hong Kong

10 9 8 7 6 5 4 3 2 1

DEDICATION

We dedicate this book to the spirit that inspires stitchers and other craftspeople to share so freely of themselves, their skills, and their friendship on the Web. By sharing we open new worlds in the hearts and minds of others, including strangers we may never meet. We also grow friendships that are irreplaceable—well, like our own!

Judy & Gloria

We hope *Free Stuff for Stitchers on the Internet* will get you started exploring and enjoying the Web like many needle artists are doing already. There are thousands of Web sites for stitchers, and the number grows daily. We could not include them all in this book, although we would have liked to. We sifted and sorted and came up with those that we think offer valuable information to stitchers. That doesn't mean there aren't many others out there that are equally illuminating and valuable. Also, because of the fluid nature of the Internet, it is inevitable that some of the Web sites listed may have moved or even vanished. Had we included only those Web sites that are sure to be around many moons from now, this book wouldn't be nearly as valuable.

Symbols in this book

 While you can find lots of free goodies on the internet, you can learn more if you participate in the many eclectic discussion groups offered on the Web.

 This icon signifies a bit of Judy-and-Gloria hard-earned wisdom—in other words, something we wished we knew when we first started cruising the Web.

 When you see this icon, read carefully—and don't make one of the same silly mistakes we have!

 This icon means that the Web site also sells products that relate to the information on their site.

Table of Contents

find Needlecraft Information on the Web!

Remember how you used to scour library shelves for books with directions on how to perform some obscure knitting stitch or graph bargello needlepoint? You don't have to do that anymore. The answers to all your stitching questions are as near as your computer.

Believe it when we say you can find anything on the Web. From crochet patterns for Barbie Doll clothes to charts of the latest embroidery floss colors from Anchor and DMC. From secrets of 19th century lacemakers to illustrated glossaries of knitting terms. From free cross-stitch charts to spinning how-tos. From illustrated tutorials of long-forgotten forms of needle weaving to earthy compendiums of advice on how to dye with pokeberries. You'll even find advice on how to buy sheep's fleece for spinning.

For whatever you want to stitch, weave, dye, or spin you'll find directions on the Web, plus more advice on what materials you will need to do it.

◑ THIS BOOK WILL DO MORE THAN GET YOU STARTED

Literally hundreds of thousands of Web sites offer free stitching patterns and advice. We've sifted through enough to make our eyes weary and siphoned them into a selection of Web sites that we think are wonderful, useful, and illuminating. Sure, you could find these sites yourself through a Web searcher—if you searched long enough, and visited lots of not-so-wonderful Web sites in the process. (Try searching on a phrase like "American Girls," as in the Pleasant Co. dolls. You'll get hundreds of Web sites for "American girls," but surely not the ones you'd expect.) And even if you spend hours on the Web, you most likely won't find all the goodies, because free stuff is getting harder to find.

Fortunately we've done all the work for you. We've also tried to select sites that have a history of longevity—in other words, they're not likely to disappear tomorrow. We hate it as much as you do when we pick up an Internet guide and none of the Web addresses are valid any longer.

And if you're like us, it's almost inevitable that the day after you find that terrific Web site with a tutorial on Brazilian embroidery or instructions for crocheting mirrors to your belly-dancing costume (ahem), you then lose your browser's book-marks. (Perhaps you upgrade your software, or your spouse attempts a mail merge from inside Windows' registry, or you just get mad at America Online and delete it from your disk.) We find it handy to have all the Web sites we like listed in a little book near at hand.

◯ GET WIRED WITHOUT ENDING UP IN TANGLES

The number of ways you can get on the Internet grows every year. You can tap in through WebTV, through cable, through America Online, and even, in some areas of the country, through your phone company. You can also tap in for free through computers available at many local libraries. If you don't know which route to take, here's our advice:

Try America Online First If You've Never Been Online

The easiest way to get on the Net is to pop into your comput-er's drive one of the free startup diskettes from America Online (**http://www.aol.com**). You can get a startup disk by calling 800/827-6364, or have a friend download the software for you from the Web.

Once you've installed the software and have connected to America Online, press Ctrl-K, or Command-K on a Mac, and type the keyword *internet*<enter> or *web*<enter>, and you're on the Internet.

The disadvantages of AOL include hourly fees to access some areas of the service and the fact that the service's access numbers are long-distance calls for some. Also, AOL's numbers are some-times busy in the evening. AOL also charges additional hourly access fees for anyone connecting from outside the continental United States or anyone calling through an AOL 800 number.

Hunt for a Local ISP for the Cheapest Rates

Many people graduate from AOL to an Internet service provider (ISP) with local access numbers. Whether you sign up with a national ISP like Earthlink (**http://www.earthlink.net**) or a local one, shop for one with a fast connection of T1 or better directly into the Internet's network backbone and 56K bps connections that support the same connection standard as your modem does. Ask whether telephone support is available in the evening and the service offers online help documents. Ask friends and neighbors for recommendations (you don't want an ISP that inflicts busy signals or is slow at delivering e-mail), or visit TheList (**http://www.thelist.com**). Most ISPs offer unlimited Internet access for $20/month, which usually includes the ability to set up a Web site.

Cable TV Offers High Speed Internet, But At a Price

Many local cable TV franchises offer Internet access through the same cable that sends you cable TV. With advertised connect rates of 10 megabytes per second, it's no wonder cable Internet is getting popular—although actual connect rates are considerably lower depending upon what time of day you tap in. Cable Internet costs about $150 for installation, plus $40 to $50 per month. (That may be a good deal if you're getting gouged by local phone rates to call AOL or an ISP.) Cable Internet is presently available in limited areas of the country, though access is sure to grow. To find out if you can get it call your local cable TV franchise. When you call for prices ask how many outlets are included in the installation fee (cable TVs and cable modems can't connect to the same outlet), and make sure you can actually connect to the Internet before your cable installer leaves.

Satellite Is Pricey, But the Only Option in Some Rural Areas

If phone calls to the nearest ISP are eating into your lifestyle and cable Internet isn't available in your area—or, if you're like some stitchers we know who've retired to life on a boat—consider accessing the Internet via satellite. The main requirements are a Windows 95/98 or NT-running PC, a direct line-of-sight to the southern horizon, and a lot of patience. Hughes Network

Tips for Accessing the Internet through Cable

Because we think cable may just become the preferred way to surf the Web in the new millennium, we've put together some tips on how to get a good connection and keep it working.

Cut a Deal—Cable companies frequently offer deals for low-cost installation—and in fact, some may even install it for free if the service is new to your area, if you dicker, and if you invoke the name of your local computer user's group.

Ask for a Second Address—Depending upon how your cable Internet connection is set up, you may be able to ask your cable company for a second gateway address. What that means is that if the gateway your cable modem normally uses to connect to the Web is slow you can detour it to a faster address.

Don't Use Junk—We all have them: spouses who accumulate boxes of cable wiring and connectors. Don't use that junk. If you're a do-it-yourselfer, or you live with one, buy all cables, splitters, and amplifiers from the cable company. The stuff they sell is designed to work with their system. The stuff you buy at mall electronics stores usually doesn't.

Call the Cable Guy If You Want the Computer and TV to Share Cable—If you want the computer and your TV to share a cable connection all you need is a splitter and some coaxial, right? No. If you use a splitter to split the cable signal going to your modem and attach it to your TV, neither your TV nor Internet picture will look good. A cable modem's signal must travel two ways, so it's unfiltered, while a video signal must be filtered. Also, a standard splitter will diminish the strength of the signal going to both cable and TV. You can always string a cable from your TV back out to where the cable company splits the signal coming into your house, at your cable box. But the best solution is to wrest the monkey wrench from your spouse before he tries it and ask the cable company to do it.

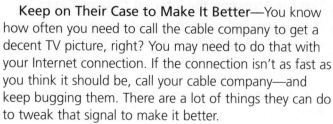

Keep on Their Case to Make It Better—You know how often you need to call the cable company to get a decent TV picture, right? You may need to do that with your Internet connection. If the connection isn't as fast as you think it should be, call your cable company—and keep bugging them. There are a lot of things they can do to tweak that signal to make it better.

Discover the Web After Hours—How fast you can connect to the Web will depend upon how many other people in your neighborhood are surfing at the time (sad but true). For the fastest connect speeds surf when everyone else is sleeping or at work.

System's DirecPC (**http://www.direcpc.com**) is the leading satellite Internet service. Cost runs about $300 for the antenna and software, plus a $50 startup fee, and $50 per month. You'll probably need to spend another $200–$300 to get the antenna installed properly on your roof (aiming it is much harder than aiming a TV satellite dish).

You'll also need to sign up for an ISP. You'll probably want a national one, and also one that has actually been tested with satellite transmission. You also want an ISP that permits subscribers to access their mail and newsgroups by an account other than one on their system. You can access AOL through a satellite link, but you'll need to use an ISP as an intermediary.

Many people love DirecPC, others hate it (tech support is lousy). If you sign-up, tap into the Usenet newsgroup **alt.satellite.direcpc** for support.

WHAT ABOUT "FREE E-MAIL" SERVICES?

There are two types of free e-mail services. There is Juno (**http://www.juno.com**) which gives you free software that you use to dial local access numbers and send and retrieve mail. And, there are Web-based services like Microsoft's Hotmail (**http://www.hotmail.com**). You tap into these Web services through a computer that already has some Internet access—a work computer for instance, or one at a library or cyber-cafe.

Their advantage is that you can send and retrieve private e-mail through the service without using, for instance, your work e-mail address if you're tapping in through your work computer.

Juno is a great deal, especially if there's a local access number in your area. In fact, many branches of the military recommend it as an economical way for military families to e-mail loved ones stationed abroad. But all you get is e-mail, unless you up $20/month for Web access.

ANATOMY OF A WEB BROWSER

Whether you tap into the Web through an Internet service, America Online, or a cable or satellite connection, the software centerpiece of your Web surfing will be what's called a browser. In the old days you needed different sorts of software to do

Be Security Conscious

When your computer is connected to the Net via cable it's basically a node in the wide-area network of your neighborhood. Because certain cable modems forward on to that network the NetBios protocol, occasionally users of certain cable Internet services have found they have access to their neighbors' hard drives. The cable service can deploy various security techniques to prevent that, but you need to take precautions too. Turn off Windows 95/98's printer and file sharing by clicking Start**Settings**Control Panel. Double-click the Network icon. Click the File and Print Sharing button. Uncheck the boxes "I want to be able to give others access to my files" and "I want to be able to allow others to print to my printer(s)." Click OK. If you're running Windows 95/98 you should also download from the Microsoft Web site (**http://www.microsoft.com**) and install the Windows 95/98 Service Pack, which includes security fixes. If you're using a Mac, head to the Control Panel and select File Sharing. Make sure it's off.

different things on the Net. For instance, you needed mail soft-ware to send and receive e-mail; a newsreader to read public discussions; you needed special software called FTP for "file download protocol" to download files to your computer. Plus you needed a browser to view (or browse through) the graphi-cal portion of the Internet known as the Web. Now all those functions are built into browsers.

Most computers are sold with Netscape's Navigator or Micro-soft's Internet Explorer already installed. You can also download them for free from Netscape's Web site (**http://www.netscape.com**) or Microsoft's (**http://www.microsoft.com**).

While you can use just about any computer to log onto the Internet in some fashion (even an original Apple II circa 1979), to be able to view graphics, you'll need a computer manufactured in at least the last 8 years. If you have an older computer, download a copy of the $35 Opera browser (**http://www.operasoftware.com**) which will run on any Windows 3.x-running PCs as old as 386SX's with 6 megabytes of RAM.

If you're running an older Macintosh, head to Chris Adams' Web Browsers for Antique Macs web page (**http://www.edprint.demon.co.uk/se/macweb.html**) and download Tradewave's MacWeb or an early version of NCSA Mosaic.

If you've never configured Internet software before, you'll need someone to help you, even if you're a computer genius (believe us, we know). Your ISP will (or should) give you direc-tions on how to set up Windows 95/98 or the Macintosh OS to at least log on to their service.

But once you're connected, you're pretty much on your own. That's why we've put together this little tutorial.

The following directions are for Explorer 4.0 and 5.0 and Navigator 4.0 but, with the exception of the instructions for e-mail, most will work with previous versions of the browsers.

HOW TO TAP INTO A WEB PAGE

To get to a Web page, type its address, also known as its URL, or Universal Resource Locator, into the Address: bar in Navigator, or the Location: bar in Internet Explorer. (In older Web browsers you must preface the address with http: as in **http://www.textiles.org**, but in new browsers you can type simply **www.textiles.org** or even **textiles.org**.)

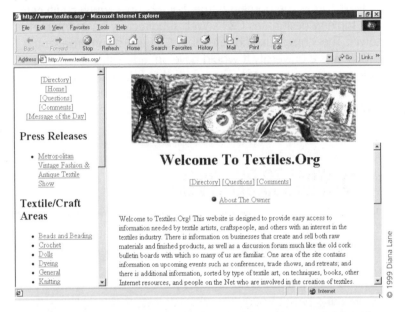

© 1999 Diana Lane

Take note that the case of the letters is important; whether the letters are all uppercase or lowercase or a combination of both.

You can also cut and paste URLs from other documents into the address or location bar. (Highlight the address with your mouse, press Ctrl-C, or Command-C on a Mac, then place the mouse in the location bar and press Ctrl-V, or Command-V on a Mac, to paste it in. Then hit <Enter>.)

Metropolitan
Vintage Fashion &
Antique Textile
Show

To move to other pages in the Web site, click on highlighted words, or, whenever your mouse cursor changes into a hand when its positioned on an object, right-click your mouse to go there.

❓ What Does All that Gobbledygook in a URL Mean?

The http: tells your Internet service what kind of document you are trying to access on the Internet. HTTP stands for "hyper-text transfer protocol," the protocol of the Web. You might run into ftp: which stands for "file transfer protocol," an early Internet scheme for transferring files. The protocol is always followed by // which separates it from the document's address.

Next comes the domain name. For example, **www.ctpub.com**. The triple-w designates C&T's Web subdirectory on its Internet server. The .com suffix indicates that C&T is a commercial entity. If C&T was a university it would have an .edu suffix or an .org one if it was a non-profit. The words that follow the domain name, separated by slashes, designate further subdirectories. Many, though not all, URLs end with a specific file name.

✋ WHAT TO DO WHEN A WEB ADDRESS FAILS

URLs point you to directories on a remote computer just like directory paths (c:\windows\programs) get you to different directories and subdirectories on your computer's hard disk.

If a Web address doesn't get you to what you want, try working back through the URL. For instance, Jerry Gentry's Silk Ribbon Web site (**http://www.ribbonworks.com**) offers a free silk ribbon newsletter **Silk Ribbon Talk** at **http://www.ribbonworks.com/newslett/newslet.html**

But if it's not there when you get there, try:
http://www.ribbonworks.com/newslet
Or:
http://www.ribbonworks.com

● HOW TO FIND PATTERNS, PEOPLE, PRODUCTS, AND MORE!

Looking for a mitten pattern? How about a friend with whom you shared your favorite crochet hook at Woodstock? To quickly find what—or who you're looking for on the Internet, all you need to do is head to one of these big searchers:

EXCITE
http://www.excite.com

ALTAVISTA
http://www.altavista.com

DOGPILE
http://www.dogpile.com

WHOWHERE? PEOPLE FINDER
http://www.whowhere.lycos.com

SWITCHBOARD PEOPLE FINDER
http://www.switchboard.com

Type the name of the pattern or person you're looking for— or even the name of a recipe or rare disease—and the searcher will come up with a list of possibly applicable Web sites or directory hits. Usually you can find at least one information-chocked Web site within the first two "pages" of matches. From that page you can scuttle around the Web to related links and Web pages.

Internet Explorer comes with some versions of America Online's software, but you can use Netscape's Navigator instead if you prefer (and many people do). Here's how: dial up AOL and make the connection. Minimize America Online's software. Fire up Navigator. Type the Web address you want to head to and you're there.

◑ HOW TO PRINT WEB PAGES, OR SELECTIONS FROM PAGES

You can print entire Web pages just like you'd print any other document on your computer screen.

First, wait until the page is transmitted completely to your computer. In Navigator you'll see what looks like snow falling through the big 'N' logo in the top right-hand corner of the screen. If you're using a Mac you'll see shooting stars.

COMMON ERROR MESSAGES WHEN YOU ENTER A WEB ADDRESS

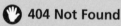 **404 Not Found**

The requested URL /blocks/tips.html was not found on this server.

Reason: Your browser was able to find the Internet service or the computer on which the Web site was or is hosted, but no such page was found on the service. (The very last word "word" at the end of a URL is the page's address. For example "tips.html.") Maybe the Web site owner removed that particular page. Or perhaps the Web site no longer exists.

Fix: Try working back through the URL as explained on page 14, to see if you can locate the Web site, or determine if the site itself is gone from the service. Also, try suffixing the page's address with "htm" or "html" instead of its current extension. For example, in place of tips.html type tips.htm. (An HTML suffix is the same as an HTM, but some Web page hosting services require that Web pages be named with one or the other. Typing the wrong extension is a common mistake.)

✋ **DNS Lookup Failure** or
Unable to locate the server. The server does not have a DNS entry.

Reason: DNS stands for "domain name server." A domain name is the first part of a URL—for instance, in **www.ctpub.com**, ctpub.com is the domain name. Every Internet service (and AOL) has a database of such Web

That means the page is being transmitted to your computer. In Explorer, the 'e' logo in the top right-hand corner spins as the page is downloading.

To print, in Navigator, pull down the File menu and select Print Preview. Once you click the Print button in the Preview window, you'll get a dialog box in which you can choose which pages of the currently viewed Web page you wish to print. On a Macintosh, pull down the File menu and select Print.

In Internet Explorer pull down the File menu and select Print.

page host addresses. When you type a URL, the first thing your browser does is tell your Internet service to look up the domain name in its database, to find out where it's located. If it can't find it, your Internet service's computer may poll other domain name directories around the Internet to determine if any of them know where the domain name can be found. If none of them do, you may get the error message "DNS Lookup Failure."

Why can't they find the domain name? Maybe it no longer exists. Or perhaps it's so new that the domain name databases your Internet service uses can't find it. Sometimes you also get this error message when there's heavy traffic on the Internet. Your Internet service is taking too long to look up the name, so your browser errors out.

Fix: Try typing the URL into your browser later in the day. If you still get the error message, try the URL a few days or even a week later. If you still get error messages the domain name no longer exists.

✋ No Response from Server

Reason: Your browser is unable to get a timely response from the Web site's host computer. This can be because of heavy traffic on the Internet, or on the branch of the Internet you are traveling. It can be because the computer that's hosting the Web site is overloaded (everyone is tapping in). Or it can be because your Internet service is overloaded, or its own computers are experiencing slowdowns for technical reasons.

Fix: Try the URL either in a few minutes, or later in the day.

On more complex Web sites your browser might ask you to specify which frame you'd like to print. A frame is a division of the page (a page with multiple frames is usually framed by multiple scroll bars, like those pictured in the Diana Lane's Textiles.Org page). You will need to go back to the page and mouse-click the side or section you wish to print then head back to the printing menu to print it.

Diana Lane's Textile.Org Web site has frames—or divisions that you can click between and scroll through individually. In order to print the book list on a framed page you must first click on the side of the page you wish to print in order to select it, then

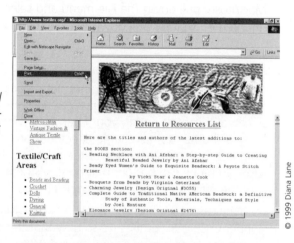

© 1999 Diana Lane

select Print or Print Preview from your browser's File menu.

Internet Explorer gives you the option of printing just the selected frame, all the frames on the Web page, or the entire Web page as you see it in your browser.

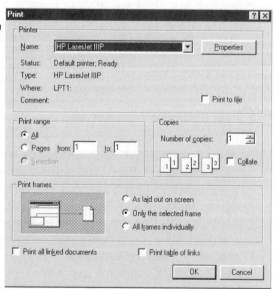

You can also print sections of a Web page by highlighting with your mouse the sections you wish to print, copying it into the clipboard, then pasting it into your word-processor and printing it there. This page shows knitting needle-sizing hints on Lois Baker's FiberLink Web site **http://www.benefitslink.com/knit/knitlink/needles.shtml**.

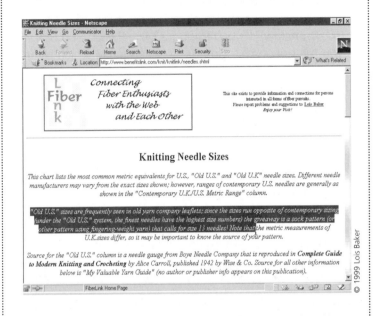

© 1999 Lois Baker

Remember, Web Pages Are Copyrighted! Web pages are copyrighted just as any publication is. Or any needlework design, for that matter. You should not print them except for your own personal use without asking permission from the Web page's owner. The same holds true for any elements on the page, including text, but also graphics. Never, ever print or distribute these things—or, heaven forbid, put them on your own Web page.

⬤ HOW TO SAVE WEB PAGES TO YOUR COMPUTER'S DISK

You can save entire Web pages to your disk so that you can peruse them later, but please heed the following warning—these pages are copyrighted and you should not distribute them.

First the page must be completely loaded.

Remember to click on the frame you wish to save.

In your browser, from the File menu select Save as... A pop-up box will give you a choice of saving the page as HTML or text (shown below). If you're using a Mac, the pop-up box will give you the option of saving the text as source, which is the same as HTML.

HTML is the coding that is used to format Web pages—it's similar to text, but with a few weird notations thrown in. Save the page in HTML format if you plan to view it later with your browser while you're off-line. (To view it in your browser later, from the File menu select Open Page. On a Mac, select Open Page in Navigator. Click Choose File, and then click your way to the file stored on your hard disk. Once you've found it, click the Open button.)

If you want to merely pull up the Web page's text in your word processor, and perhaps print it later, save it as Text.

Your browser will let you save Web pages either as plain text or with their HTML formatting, but neither option will save graphics. You'll need to save each image individually.

In order to save a picture off the Web, right click on it in Windows or click-hold on a Mac and select Save as... Remember though that these images are copyrighted by their artist and you should not print or distribute them without asking permission first.

Neither of these features will let you save the page's images, however. To save the graphics you need to:

Position your cursor over each image you wish to save, and right-click. On a Mac, click-hold. A menu box will pop up. Select Save Image As... or Save Picture As... Save it into the same directory as you saved the page's HTML code.

● HOW TO CAPTURE IMAGES YOU FIND ON THE INTERNET

Images on Web pages are copyrighted as text is. If you want to use them in any way—either to print to distribute to your friends or post on your own Web pages—the same rules apply as to text: you need to ask the owner's permission first!

Position your cursor over the image and right-click. On a Mac click-hold. A menu box will pop up. Select Save Image As... or Save Picture As...

You can later view it in either your browser or a graphics program like Paint Shop Pro. You can even import it into a word processing document. (In Microsoft Word, from the Insert menu select Picture.)

⬤ HOW TO DOWNLOAD SOFTWARE FROM THE INTERNET

In most instances all you need to do is mouse-click on the high-lighted name of the program or file on a Web page and your browser will start downloading—hopefully by prompting you where you want to store the file (shown below).

But sometimes that doesn't work. If that happens, right-click in Windows or click-hold on a Mac on the name of the file. When a pop-up menu appears, click on Save Link As... and the browser will begin downloading.

*You can download a demo of the cross-stitch chart-ing program Pattern Maker from the Hobbyware Web site (**http://www. hobbyware.com**). In most instances all you need to do is click on a high-lighted program or file name in order to download it.*

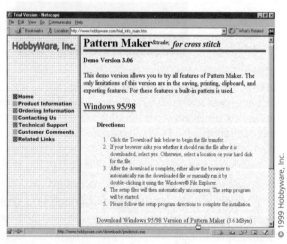

Once you click on the file name your browser will ask you where on your computer you want to store the software. Once you select a direc-tory, click Save.

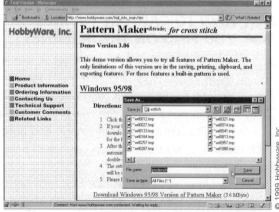

Once the file begins transferring, this box will pop up, showing you the progress of the download.

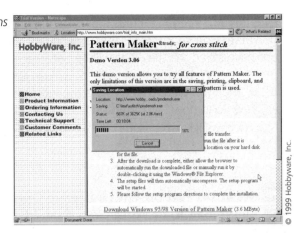

© 1999 Hobbyware, Inc.

Say you can't get your browser to download software in a sane fashion. Maybe it spits kooky characters across the screen when you try. There's a simple way out: right-click in Windows, or click-hold on a Mac, on the file name so this menu box pops up. Select Save Link As... and you'll be on your way.

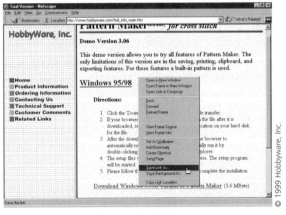

© 1999 Hobbyware, Inc.

Should the file transfer progress box (shown above, top) disappear, don't panic. Its disappearance does not mean your computer has stopped downloading the file. For instance, sometimes it disappears if you click on something else on the Web page or in your browser. You will probably find the transfer box tucked away in some other corner of your computer screen (like the bottom program status bar) and the transfer still faithfully chugging away in the background.

One thing to keep in mind is that if the file transfer progress box flashes on your screen, then disappears, your browser may not have saved the file. That will be because it's not tapped into the correct Web page to actually download the file. You should be on the Web page that displays the highlighted file name, or a "Download now" link. In other words, you need to be only one mouse click away from the file download in order to get this to work.

What Do You Do With Software Once You Download It, or What Does That ZIP or SIT at the End of Its Name Mean?

When you download software from a Web site it's usually compressed. That means that the file has been shrunk so that it takes less time to transfer to your computer.

PKZIP by PKWare (**http://www.pkware.com**) is the most commonly used compression format in the PC world. When a file has a .ZIP extension it has been compressed with PKZIP. You'll need to download PKZIP in order to uncompress it. A handy (in fact indispensable) utility to have is the $29 shareware program WinZip by Nico Mak (**http://www.winzip.com**). It will de-ZIP those files for you automatically.

Stuffit, a free program by Aladdin Software (**http://www.aladdinsys.com**), is the compression program used with Macintoshes. Software compressed with Stuffit ends with .SIT, and you'll need to download Stuffit in order to expand it.

What about files ending with .EXE? They're self-extracting, which means that you merely click on them in order to uncompress them.

As a file download starts, always check that the file is writing itself to your disk with the same name as it's stored on the remote computer, so you know what to do with it.

HOW TO SEND E-MAIL

If you're using America Online all you need to do is click on the You Have Mail icon on the greeting screen to read your e-mail or send mail, even out on the Internet. (To send messages to someone on the Internet from AOL, type the full Internet address—for example ctinfo@ctpub.com—into the To: line in the AOL mail screen just as you'd type an AOL address.)

If you're using an Internet service you can use special mail software like Eudora or Pegasus. Or, you can use the mail program built into your browser.

In Navigator, press Ctrl-2 to get to the mail box (shown at right). On a Mac, click the Mail icon box in the lower-right hand corner of the browser's screen to get to your in-box. Command-T retrieves new e-mail.

In Explorer, click the Mail icon in the upper right-hand corner of the browser's screen to load the Outlook Express mail program.

Press Ctrl-2 in Windows to get to your mail in Navigator.

▶ Unfortunately, You Will Need to Set Up Your Browser's Mail Program to Be Able to Send Mail

In order for your browser to send and retrieve mail through your ISP for the first time, you'll need to tell it the name of your ISP's computer where it stores mail. You can probably guess the name of this computer. Its probably named "mail." For instance, if your e-mail address is sue@biginternet.com, Big Internet's mail computer is probably named mail.biginternet.com.

Maybe not. Regardless, your Internet service should tell you the name of the computer where it stores mail so you can enter this vital information into your mail program. That, your Internet e-mail address and password are essentially all the browser needs to know to be able to send and receive mail.

▶ Setting Up Navigator

From Navigator's Edit menu select Preferences. Under the Mail & Groups category, select Mail Server. Type in your user name on the ISP, and the names of the incoming and outgoing mail servers. Click OK when you're finished.

You can set up Navigator to send and retrieve mail through your ISP by heading to this setup box. Get to it by selecting Preferences from the Edit menu, then scrolling through the setup menu list on the left.

▶ Setting Up Explorer

In Explorer's Outlook Express, from the Tools menu select Accounts. Click the Add button and select Mail to start the wizard that will guide you through the mail set-up process. When you're done you should have settings like those shown below.

When Outlook Express is set up successfully to send and retrieve mail, you should have a settings box similar to this (you can reach it by pulling down the Tools menu and selecting Accounts. Head to the Mail tab, highlight the account name, and click the Properties button). Judy's e-mail address is judyheim@execpc.com, so notice that her outgoing SMTP mail server is named—you guessed it, mail.execpc.com. Even if your ISP gave you erro-neous directions for setting up your mail program, you can make a few simple deductions from your e-mail address to fill in the blanks.

▶ Sending and Receiving Mail with Navigator

Press Ctrl-2 to get to Navigator's mail program. On a Mac, click the Mail icon box in the lower-right hand corner of the browser's screen. To download your mail from your Internet ser-vice, click the Get Msg icon, and then type your ISP password when prompted.

To send a message, click the New Msg icon. After you're fin-ished writing, click the Send icon to dial your ISP and send it immediately. Or pull down the File menu and select Send Later for Navigator to store it in its outbox.

You can write your message in different fonts and colors with Navigator's mail program. You can even add pictures by heading to the Insert menu and selecting Image. But your recipient won't be able to see the special effects unless they're using another HTML-compatible mail program like that in Explorer.

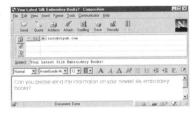

Sending and Receiving Mail with Explorer

Head to Outlook Express by clicking the Mail icon in Explorer's right-hand corner. Press Ctrl-N, or Command-N on a Mac, to pop up a message composition form. When you're done writing, click the Send button. Take note that this will only store it in Outlook's Outbox. To actually send it you need to click the Send and Receive button on the top of Outlook's main screen so that the program dials your Internet service and checks and sends mail.

HOW CAN YOU TALK TO OTHER STITCH-A-HOLICS ON THE INTERNET?

There are several ways besides e-mail in which you can talk to stitchers around the world.

Message Boards on Web Sites—

Many stitching Web sites offer message or bulletin boards where you can post and read messages on topics ranging from floss brands to knitting techniques. Often these discussions are lively and informative, because they're so easy to tap into and they remain on the Web site for so long. All you need to join in is to type the URL into your browser.

Usenet Newsgroups—

Newsgroups are public messages that swirl through the Internet in bulletin-board style. There are seven specifically devoted to textiles:

rec.crafts.textiles.misc
rec.crafts.textiles.marketplace
rec.crafts.textiles.quilting
rec.crafts.textiles.yarn

rec.crafts.textiles.machine-knit
rec.crafts.textiles.needlework
rec.crafts.textiles.sewing

As you can see they are named like subdirectories on a computer. To tap in you'd use the news feature of your browser, or special news reading software.

🖱 Mailing Lists—

You'll find dozens of mailing lists devoted to different stitching topics. Mailing lists are also where you find the most worthwhile information on the Internet on just about any topic.

You don't tap into a Web site to participate. You send an e-mail message to a computer (or person) to subscribe to the list. Each day e-mail from other members of the mailing list finds its way to your mailbox. To participate in the discussion

---

❓ HOW SAFE IS THE INTERNET?

Everytime Judy's mom hears that her daughter's been surfing the Web, she gasps, "Be careful! That Internet is not safe!"

The Internet is safer than the average subway station—but sometimes not by much. We know you're an adult and will take care of yourself just as you would in a subway station. But just so you know we're concerned about your safety, just like Judy's mother is of her daughter's, here are the major Judy-and-Gloria warnings:

• *Never give anyone your credit card number,* any of your online passwords, or any personal information such as your street address or phone number. An all-too-common ruse is for hackers to e-mail a new subscriber to America Online alleging they are a representative of AOL and need the subscriber to resubmit their credit card number for verification. Hackers sent Gloria instant messages requesting her password. (She copied and pasted the messages into an e-mail, then she sent it to AOL management at the complaint box at TOSSPAM.) Another ploy is for hackers to claim they work for Microsoft and to e-mail victims a "security patch" for Internet Explorer. Once the "security

---

you send your message to a central computer that broadcasts it to everyone on the list.

Online Service Discussion Forums—
All the major online services, including America Online, CompuServe, and Microsoft Network, offer lively stitching discussion forums.

Chat Rooms—
Aren't chat rooms those notorious dens where lascivious strangers type to each other at 2 a.m.? Yes, but stitchers also enjoy getting together to chat, both on the Internet and on online services like America Online and CompuServe.

---

patch" is installed it e-mails to the hackers the victim's passwords. No company ever e-mails a security patch!

• *Beware of get-rich-quick offers* that arrive by the megabyte in your e-mail box. And never answer junk e-mail. You'll either be bombarded with more e-mail, or the sender may retaliate if you ask to be removed from their mailing list. (That happened to a prominent woman in the crafts industry. An angry junk e-mailer mail-bombed her company's e-mail server after she asked to be removed from his mailing list.)

• *If you shop on the Web,* pay with a credit card in case there are problems. Never type your credit card into any Web site that's not a "secure" Web site. That means that the site will encrypt the information you send it. As you enter a secure site your browser will tell you that it's secure. Also, Navigator will display a lock icon.

• *Be sure to supervise your children* on the Net—the best way is to talk to them regularly about what they're doing online. Warn them, as often as you can, not to meet in person strangers they may meet online, even if they insist the new friend is a teenager—sometimes they're not.

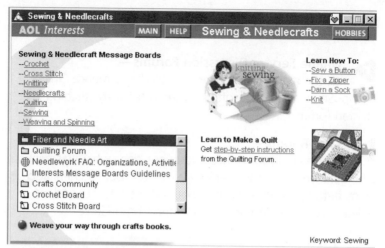

You'll find other stitchers on America Online in the crafts center. You'll also find pattern libraries, message boards, and software. To get there use the keyword (Ctrl-K, or Command-K on a Mac) "crafts" or "needlecraft."

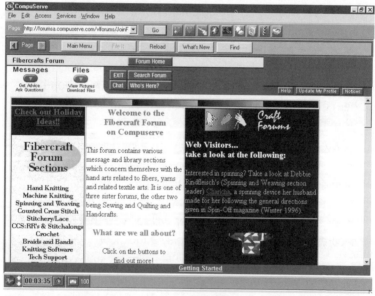

CompuServe's Fibercrafts forum is host to many avid chatters. To join head to the forum by using the "go" word (click the green light icon) "fibercrafts."

HOW TO READ USENET NEWSGROUPS WITH YOUR WEB BROWSER

Participating in Web site message boards or mailing lists is fairly straightforward, so long as you know how to use your Web browser and mail program. But setting up your browser to read newsgroups can be tricky. The first time you want to read a newsgroup you'll need to download from your Internet service a list of current newsgroups. Then you'll need to search it and subscribe to the groups you're interested in. Finally, you need to download the messages themselves. Here's how to do it with Navigator and Explorer:

Can you (or should you) send e-mail messages festooned with pictures and color? The mail programs found in the latest versions of Explorer and Navigator are what's called HTML or rich text compatible. That means you can use them to send—and read mail with the same kind of formatting found on Web pages. And the same sorts of pictures too—like GIF and JPG images.

America Online can also send and read *some* HTML coding in messages, but not all.

Should you bedeck your e-mail with pictures of pictures of yourself and your knitting projects? Probably not.

First, graphics take *much* longer than text to download. And no one likes to sit twiddling their fingers as their mail program chugs to capture some humongous e-mail message they were not expecting.

Second, many people use text-only e-mail programs like Eudora that will display that rich text as gibberish.

Maybe this will change someday. Maybe everyone will have super-fast links into the Internet and HTML-friendly e-mail programs. Until then, write your messages in old-fashioned plain text. (That means avoiding Explorer's "stationary" feature, and turning off the rich text setting. You can find it by pulling down the Tools menu and selecting Options. Under the Send tab, check Plain Text, then click the Apply button.)

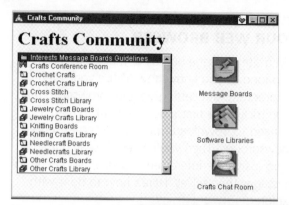

You can chat with other stitchers on America Online in the Crafts Community chat room. To get there use the keyword "crafts." To get the weekly schedule click the Crafts Chat Room button.

© 1999 Barbara Breiter. This feature is reprinted with permission from Barbara Breiter, a Guide at Miningco.com, Inc. It can be found on the Web at www.Miningco.com. To follow this series at Barbara's site on Knitting go to knitting.miningco.com.

Many needlecrafts Web sites host regular chats. To join in you may need to download special chat software (if you do there will be directions on the Web site). Chats are a regular feature of the Mining Co.'s needlecraft sites, such as the knitting one. To participate you need only to be running version 3.x or higher of Netscape or Internet Explorer, and you must have Java enabled.

How to Read the Usenet Stitching Newsgroups with Navigator

1. You must first set up your browser to retrieve newsgroups from your Internet server. Find out from your Internet server the name of the computer where newsgroups are stored. (It will be something like groups.myisp .com.) Pull down the Edit menu and select Preferences. Under Mail & Groups, head to the Group Server setup box and enter your ISP information. Click OK to save it.

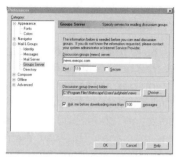

First you need to tell Navigator the name of the server on your ISP where newsgroups are stored.

2. Connect to your Internet service.

3. Head to Navigator's message center by pressing Ctrl-2 or click the Mail icon box in the lower-right hand corner of the browser's screen on a Mac.

4. From the File menu, select Subscribe to Discussion Groups.

5. Click the All Groups tab to download a list of current newsgroups. This may take a while since the list is large. The message "Receiving discussion groups" should appear on the very bottom line of the screen.

You need to download the complete list of newsgroups in order to search for the needlework ones.

6. When that humongous list of newsgroups has finished downloading, head to the Search for a Group tab. Type "crafts" in the search box (or whatever you're interested in) and click the Search Now button. Type "textiles" instead to get a full list of all the needlecraft-related newsgroups.

7. Once the newsgroup searcher has come up with a list of interesting newsgroups, highlight the one you want to read (shown below), and press the Subscribe button. A check will appear beside it.

8. To read your newsgroup, head back to the message center (Ctrl-2 or click the Mail icon box on a Mac). From the pull-down menu box at the top of the screen, select the newsgroup and click Download Messages. You may want to download only a selection (under 500 for example) and mark as read the rest of the messages. This way, the next time you download messages from the newsgroup, you will only download the newest ones.

9. From the Go menu you can move from thread to thread, reading messages and skipping others.

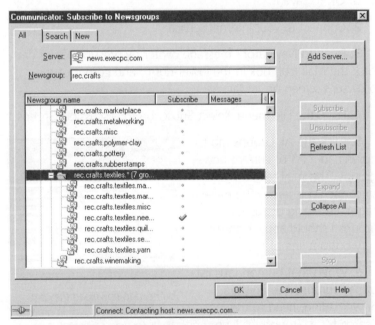

After you download and search the newsgroups, subscribe to the groups you want to read by selecting them. You can click through the list just as you'd click through subdirectories on your computer.

10. In the future to read messages, go to the message center (Ctrl-2, or click the Mail icon box on a Mac). From the pull-down menu box at the top of the screen, select the newsgroup you want to read. From the File menu select Get Messages/New.

Select the messages and message threads you want to read and they'll appear in the bottom of the screen. (If you don't get a split screen you may need to "pull up" the bottom portion of the screen with your mouse. In other words, the window is there, it's just hidden.)

Read Usenet Textile Newsgroups from Your Browser

You can read the textile newsgroups from the comfort of your Web browser by heading to **Dejanews** (**http://www.dejanews.com**). Reading them through this Web site isn't as easy as reading them with your browser's newsreader, but it's a simple way to access the groups.

How to Read the Usenet Stitching Newsgroups with Explorer

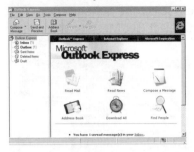

1. Load the Outlook Express mail portion of Internet Explorer by clicking on the mailbox icon on the top right-hand corner of the screen. Click the Read News icon on the Express screen. If you have not yet set it up to read newsgroups with your ISP, a setup wizard will appear. It will prompt you for your name, e-mail address, and the name of the dial-up connection you use to connect to your ISP. Most important of all it will ask you the name of the server on your ISP where the news messages can be found.

2. The next time you click Express's Read News icon it will ask you if you'd like to download a list of the newsgroups from your ISP. This may take a while since there are tens of thousands of newsgroups.

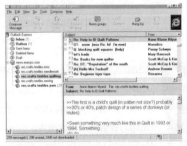

3. Type "textiles" to search the list for newsgroups that contain "textiles" in their name—and to get a full list of the needlework-related newsgroups. Subscribe to them by highlighting each, clicking the Subscribe button. Then click OK when you're done.

4. To read newsgroups that you've subscribed to, click on the name of the newsgroup on the left side of the screen. To read individual messages, click on the headers displayed at the top right of the screen.

How to Read the Usenet Stitching Newsgroups on America Online

1. *To read the Internet newsgroups through AOL press Ctrl-K, or Command-K on a Mac, and type the keyword newsgroups. Click on the Search All Newsgroups icon to search the tens of thousands of newsgroups for ones in your interests. (Some search words that work are: quilting, textiles, cross-stitch, sewing, knitting, weaving.)*

2. *Once you click the Search Newsgroups icon, type your search word and press Search. Once AOL comes up with a list of matching newsgroups, click the Add button to add selected newsgroups to the list of newsgroups that you wish to read, or click on the name of the newsgroup and from the pop-up box click "Subscribe to newsgroup."*

3. *Depending upon which version of AOL's software you're using you can read the messages in the newly subscribed newsgroup immediately, or else you'll need to head back to the main newsgroup menu by closing the windows (click the X in the upper right-hand corner). Click the Read My Newsgroups button to pop up a list of the newsgroups to which you're subscribed. Click the List Unread button to list messages in the newsgroups that you have not yet read.*

4. *To read listed messages and their replies, highlight the message and click the Read button.*

● MAILING LISTS ARE FUN, INFORMATIVE, BUT YOU NEED TO FOLLOW THE RULES

No matter what your interests, mailing lists are your best source of information on the Internet. But before you sign up for one, you should read its rules for joining and posting to the list. Then follow our tips on mailing list netiquette.

When you join a mailing list, the computer that runs the list will automatically mail you directions for participating. Print them; keep them near at hand. Take note of the list's different e-mail addresses. You will be sending mail to one address, and sending any subscription changes to a different "administrative" address. *Don't send messages to subscribe or unsubscribe to the list to the address that will broadcast your message to everyone on the list!*

You probably have only a limited amount of disk space on your ISP to store incoming e-mail. That means that if you're a member of a mailing list that generates lots of mail, the mail may overrun your mailbox if you don't check your e-mail daily. When that happens, e-mail that people send you will bounce back to them. And the list may automatically unsubscribe you because messages are bouncing back. The solution: subscribe to the digest version of the list, if one is available, and unsubscribe from the list if you're going out of town.

If the mailing list has rules about how mail to the list should be addressed, follow them. Many lists request that members include the list's name in the Subject: line of any messages so those members who have set up their e-mail software to filter messages can do so effectively. You should also try to make the Subject: line of your message as informative as possible for readers who don't have time to read every message posted to the list.

Never include your address, phone number, or other personal information in a mailing list post. Many mailing lists are archived—which means that everyone on the Internet might be able to read them until the end of time!

When replying to a message, before you hit the Send button take a look at the message's address to check where it's going. Don't send a personal reply to everyone on the mailing list. And don't hit Reply to All if the message is addressed to many different people or lists.

Here are a few mailing list terms you might encounter:

Moderated List—All messages that are mailed to the list are first sent to a moderator to screen before being broadcast to everyone on the list. No, it's not censorship, but merely a tactic to keep messages to the topic under discussion, and on some lists to prevent "flame wars" from breaking out between disagreeing members.

Unmoderated List—Messages are not screened.

Digest—Messages are collected into one long e-mail message that is sent at the end of the day to members who subscribe to the list's "digest version."

Archive—Some mailing list messages are stored in vast libraries on a Web site for others to search and read years later.

FAQ—Most lists have a "frequently asked question" file that contains questions to answers that list members commonly ask. Usually the FAQ is stored on the list's Web site, although some lists allow members to retrieve the file through e-mail.

Your computer *cannot* contract a virus by your tapping into a Web site or reading an e-mail message. Passing disks between work, school, and home computers is the most common way in which viruses are spread.

❓ THINKING OF BARGAIN HUNTING IN WEB FLEAMARKETS? READ OUR TIPS FIRST!

Web fleamarkets like **eBay** (**http://www.ebay.com**) are great spots to find old patterns, needlecraft books, supplies, and even the remains of craft projects that others have abandoned (!). Here are tips for fun (and safe) cyber-fleamarketing.

• **How safe is buying from Web fleamarkets?** It depends a *lot* on what you're buying—in our opinion. High-ticket items like consumer electronics are high risk. Remember that in most instances you're not actually buying from the fleamarket but from individuals who advertise on it. Your entire transaction will probably be with a stranger about whom you know nothing but an e-mail address. Judy often buys vintage patterns, beads, and laces on eBay, but rarely buys anything over $10. She frankly isn't too worried that someone who sells old buttons will turn out to be a con artist. She would never buy computer equipment from these sites.

• **Before you bid check the seller's buyer ratings.** Web auction sites let buyers post comments about sellers after a transaction. Although these "buyer ratings" are often not what they're cracked up to be—they can be easily forged, and aggrieved buyers may be too timid to post 'negative feed-back'—if a seller boasts hundreds of happy customers that can be a good sign that they will in fact send you your 99 cent buttons without laundering your check.

• **Never send money orders.** Some sellers accept only money orders. If you send a money order you have no way of knowing that your money actually arrived in their hands and they cashed the check.

• **Ask questions before bidding**. Never take anything for granted. If the seller maintains in their description that "all pattern pieces are intact" ask them how they know. Did they actually take them out of the package and count them? Does the package look opened? Are the instructions in one piece? Does that "Victorian lace" come with a "poly blend" tag? Find out what they plan to charge for shipping.

• **Check the "Ending Today" listings for the best buys.** Most people bid on items in the last hours or minute before an auction ends.

• **If you're looking for something particular,** like poodle-themed embroidery patterns from the '50s (Judy has a collection of those accumulated from eBay), search the entire auction site for different words, combinations of words, and shortened forms of words, and even misspellings. For instance—poodle, podle, emb, poodle pat.—will all turn up patterns with the proper qualifications. We've found quilt tops accidentally posted with the Rolex watches this way.

• **Save all correspondence with the seller.** Keep the URL of the Web page the item is posted on. And keep in mind, before you bid, that if you get ripped off you'll have little of any recourse.

• You can learn the latest on scams and security problems on Web auction sites by visiting Auction Watch (**http://www.auctionwatch.com**).

? WILL MY COMPUTER CATCH A VIRUS?

Viruses are noxious bits of program code that travel in computer files—usually program files—and plant themselves on your disk for the purpose of wreaking havoc.

The best way to avoid contracting a virus is to scan with a virus-checker any program that you download from the Internet, prior to running it. Our favorite is the $50 Norton AntiVirus from Symantec (**http://www.symantec.com**, 800/441-7234, 541/334-6054). Be sure to keep its virus database updated by downloading monthly upgrades from Symantec's Web site.

You should also scan any disk of software that you buy, or CD-ROM, prior to installing it. Several viruses have been spread through commercially distributed software.

You should be especially careful to scan any disks that have been in your work computer, or come from the computers of your child's friends.

You should not open any file attachment that comes with an e-mail message from a stranger. Delete it, and if it was ever dan-

free Stuff for Knitters

D o you miss those long afternoons you spent in your Aunt
Eda's kitchen, her wood stove crackling, her teakettle hiss-
ing, both of your knitting needles clacking as you discussed
Uncle Billy's bad knees or Aunt Lilly's bad heart? No? Let's pre-
tend that you do. The World Wide Web is full of sociable knitters who, like Aunt Eda, are always anxious to chat about their
latest project, advise one on a better way to decrease stitches in
a shoulder cap, or discourse on life in general. (Once, when
Judy stumbled on a bizarre stitch in a pattern while knitting just
before bed, she tapped in a description of her quandary into
the Internet, and within moments knitters around the world e-
mailed her directions on how to perform that peculiar stitch.)

The most famous cyber-klatch of knitters is a mailing list
discussion group called **Knit List**, which boasts thousands of
members worldwide. (You'll read more about it throughout this
chapter.) But there are many other cubbies in cyberspace where
you'll find knitting patterns, advice, references, magazines—and
of course friends.

⋈ *The Big Knitting Web Sites*

There are lots of great places for knitters on the Web. But there
are a few mega-sites that offer loads of knitting news, advice,
patterns, links to other knitting hotspots in cyberspace, and of
course good conversation with other knitters.

LOIS BAKER'S KNIT LINK
http://www.benefitslink.com/knit/KnitLink/index.shtml

*Knit Link offers links to the best of the Web's knitting resources,
including patterns, scintillating conversations, and other resources.*

KNITTING AT THE MINING CO.
http://knitting.tqn.com/

*Barbara Breiter is your guide to the world of knitting in cyberspace.
She offers a terrific guide to free knitting patterns on the Web. She
also offers discussion boards, news, feature stories, and more.*

THE ONLINE KNITTING COMPENDIUM
http://www.woolworks.org/

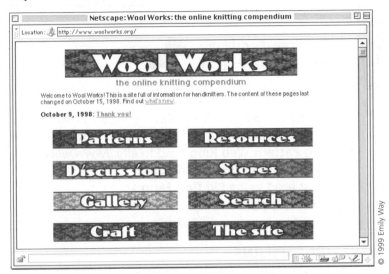

© 1999 Emily Way

Emily Way's legendary site offers discussion boards, free patterns, links, and info on joining all the knitting discussion groups around the Net, plus "frequently asked questions" files from the biggest knitting discussion list of all, Knit List.

DELPHI'S TEXTILE ARTS
http://www.delphi.com/textile

Rita Levine is the host of this venerable knitters' and fiber artists' gathering spot. It includes bulletin boards, real time chat, patterns, news, and more.

Knitting on America Online
If you're a member of AOL, use the keyword "knitting" to find your way to the klatch of knitters.

Knitting on CompuServe
If you're a member of CompuServe, use the "go" word "fibercrafts" to get to the forum of the same name. Lots of knitters hang out there, especially machine ones. That's not surprising since the forum is managed by Susan Lazear, the machine-knitting guru of Cochenille Studios.

Knitting Patterns

The Free Knitting Pattern Web Ring

Head to the Free Knitting Pattern Web Ring

A Web ring is a group of Web sites organized around a theme that link to each other. To tap into the **Free Knitting Pattern Web Ring** head to **http://www.webring.org/cgi-bin/webring?ring=knitring; list.**

Or, just head to the **Pig Dog Farm** at **http://www.pigdogfarm.com.**

KNIT LIST PATTERNS

The biggest collection of free knitting patterns on the Internet is that assembled by members of the big mailing list discussion group **Knit List** (you'll read more about them in the following pages). The collection is stored on various servers around the Internet, organized by year. A good spot to start your search is at **Emily Way's Wool Works** (http://www.woolworks.org). Also, try **Carlin's Knitting Page** (http://math.vanderbilt.edu/~cjs/patterns/).
Other URLs to try are:
http://freenet.msp.mn.us/people/campbell/knit/pat.html
http://www.keyway.net/crafts/96'Gifts.htm

These patterns are often very clever and unique, including such marvels as wrist warmers for arthritis sufferers and the "ultimate cat toy."

DOLLS AND DOLL CLOTHES PATTERNS
http://www.woolworks.org/dollpatt.html

Emily Way offers a collection of links to some very unique doll and doll clothes patterns around the Web.

CARLIN'S KNITTING PAGE
http://math.vanderbilt.edu/~cjs/knitting.html

You'll find lots of links to free patterns, plus links to personal pages of knitters, and also links to corrections for commercial patterns.

ESTHER'S KNITTING PAGE
http://www.cs.oswego.edu/~ebozak/knit/

Esther offers directions from many of her published patterns, plus references, help for aran sweater knitters, and a pattern for a custom-fit dog coat.

KNIT YOUR WAY TO GLAMOUR
http://www.interlog.com/~suzu/s_knit.htm

Don't we wish? Suzu of Ontario, Canada offers a boodle of knitting patterns from the past, including ones for men's, women's and baby's sweaters, socks, and hats, plus novelties.

🛒 KNITTING PATTERNS
FROM DOLLETTES-N-THINGS
http://www.dollette.com/

You'll find patterns for absolutely marvelous knitted dolls.

PIG DOG FARM
http://www.pigdogfarm.com/freepat.htm

The inimitable Liz Clouthier offers free patterns like the "Emergency doll gift."

CRAFT YARN COUNCIL OF AMERICA PROJECT PAGE
http://www.craftyarncouncil.com/project.html

The Yarn Council offers an ever-changing collection of patterns.

FITTED, TOE-UP SOCKS
http://www.clark.net/pub/oldsma/toesox.txt

Manny Olds, with inspiration from Liz Sommers, share instructions for socks that "fit well enough."

FREEBIES FROM COATES PATON
http://www.coatspatons.com/free/freestuf.htm

This craft products maker offers an assortment of downloadable knitting patterns including sweaters, angels, and vests. You need Adobe Acrobat to view the leaflets.

PROJECTS FROM SOLUTIA, INC.
http://www.thesmartyarns.com/project1.html

Monsanto offers a collection of marvelous sweater, afghan, and pillow patterns.

CRAFTNET VILLAGE.COM—NEEDLEWORK
http://www.craftnetvillage.com/project_library/needlework.html

Craftnet Village offers a large selection of knit projects.

TIP

Swap Patterns with Other Knitters in Cyberspace
Advertise for the ones you're looking for—and the ones
you want to give away at **Liz Clouthier's Knit Swap**
(**http://www.angelfire.com/me/knitswap/**). Judy found new
homes for about a hundred old knitting books and patterns in less than two hours on the Internet. Mailing
them all out, however, took her about three weeks.

 *Knitting References*

CHARTS AND OTHER INFORMATION FOR KNITTERS
http://www.benefitslink.com/knit/KnitLink/Useful_Charts_and_
Other_Information/index.shtml

*Lois Baker has assembled a list of links to all manner of knitting
charts around the Web, including ones on needle sizes, yarn substi-
tutions, and size and measurements. You'll also find a conversion
calculator that will convert between ounces and grams, and meters
and yards.*

FRANCY LESH'S YARN GUIDE
http://www.keyway.net/crafts/Yarnguide.htm

*Francy Lesh offers a collection of "standard information from yarn
companies" on yarn and needle size for different projects and
needs.*

KNITTING FOR DOLLS FAQ
http://www.woolworks.org/dolls.html

*Caroline McMillan has assembled a collection of sources, tech-
niques, patterns, and a book list for knitting for dolls—advice given
and collected over the years by knitters around the Internet.*

TOM'S KNITTING ONLINE
http://www.skepsis.com/~tfarrell/textiles/knit/

*Thomas M. Farrell taught himself to knit to occupy his time riding
the subway. Follow Tom's illustrated instructions and you'll learn to
knit too.*

KNITTED THREADS—TIPS AND TECHNIQUES
http://home.earthlink.net/~kthreads/tiptechs.htm

Janet Rehfeldt shares tips and information for hand and machine knitters, as well as crocheters.

WOOL MARK
http://www.woolmark.com/

© 1999 Woolmark

Did you know that more than three-quarters of the garments in the autumn/winter collections in Paris are made from wool, and most of it is Australian? That's the sort of thing you'll learn at this site from Woolmark.

Knitting Magazines
Web-based Knitting Magazines You Can Read for Free

KNITNET
http://www.knitnet.com/

This is a quarterly Web-based magazine loaded with articles and patterns. It's published by Dougal Bichan and edited by Sharon Airhart.

KNITTINGNEWS NEWSLETTER
http://craftfinder.com/html/newslist.html

This is a knitting newsletter containing patterns and advice, written by Vanessa Sanford Paradis, which will be delivered to your e-mail box.

Create a Custom Sock Pattern

Have you been searching for years for a sock pattern that will fit a triple-D foot with a skinny ankle? Head to E. Stokes Reynolds' **The Sock Calculator** (**http//www .panix .com/~ilaine/socks.html**). Type your gauge, enter your calf, knee, ankle, and foot measurements and The Sock Calculator will generate a sock pattern for you that you can print. The calculator can create either a hand or machine pattern.

 Web Sites of Print Publications

KNITTER'S
http://www.xrx-inc.com/knitters/knitters.html

VOGUE KNITTING AND FAMILY CIRCLE KNITTING
http://www.vogueknitting.com/

INTERWEAVE KNITS
http://www.interweave.com/iwpsite/knits/knits.html

KNITTING NOW
http://www.knittingnow.com/

Collections of Knitting Wisdom

Frankly we believe that the knitters on **Knit List** (a discussion group described throughout this chapter) constitute the smartest group of people in the world—not only when discoursing on knitting, but just about any other topic. Here are links to their FAQs, in which you'll find answers to questions like "Where can I get the Princess Diana sweater patterns?" and "Where on the Web can I find patterns for Teletubbies?" You'll find source lists, lots of advice, and links to free knitting patterns all over the Internet:
http://www.woolworks.org/faqproj.html
http://www.woolworks.org/faqsource.html
http://www.woolworks.org/faqtech.html
    Clifford L. Williams offers another collection of Knit List wisdom at **http://www.southern.edu/~williams/handknit.html**

Knitting Discussion Groups

KNIT LIST

As we mentioned earlier Knit List is the quintessential Internet knitting discussion group, with thousands of members. You can tap into its Web page at **http://www.kniton.com/knitlist/**. But before you join you should read the **KnitList Rules and Netiquette** (**http://www.woolworks.org/faqlist.html**). This will tell you what you can talk about, what you can't, and whether you can post your Aunt Betty's teakettle cozy pattern to the list. Since the list is so big it's important that everyone follow the rules. (One rule is that members are permitted to write to the list only once a day.)

That said, you could subscribe to the list by sending an e-mail message to majordomo@kniton.com with *subscribe knitlist* or *subscribe knitlist-digest* as the message.

If you're having problems subscribing you can send e-mail—politely—to the list's tech support Delta Force, also known as the List Moms (**listmoms@kniton.com**).

Can you post your Aunt Betty's cozy pattern? No. The List Moms do not permit posts of any patterns "found among your grandmother's things." This is why you have to read the rules.

KNITDESIGN
http://www.xws.com/terispage/design/index.html

Teri Pittman (tpittman@xws.com) runs this list to discuss sizing and design issues. To sign up head to the Web page.

AMPLE-KNITTERS
http://www.mailing-list.net/ample-knitters/

This discussion group is for plus-size knitters.

KNITTING

*This list, run by Rob McKenzie (**rmckenzi@rpmdp.com**), is also for discussing crochet, plastic canvas, and even sewing. To subscribe send an e-mail to majordomo@ml.rpmdp.com with* subscribe knitting. *as the message.*

KNITWITS

*Diane Pahl (**Diane_Pahl@classic.msn.com**) runs this list. To sign up send an e-mail message to* listserv@salata.com *with* sub knitwits *as the message.*

TECHKNIT
http://www.benefitslink.com/knit/KnitLink/Find_Knitters/Mailing_Lists/TechKnit/

Lois Baker runs this list for spinning and knitting.

 Web-based Bulletin Boards

FIBER LINK MESSAGE BOARDS
http://www.benefitslink.com/knit/

KNITTING CHAT AT THE MINING CO.
http://knitting.miningco.com/mpchat.htm

WOOL WORKS DISCUSSION BOARD
http://www.woolworks.org

Tap Into Knit List's "Lessons from the School of Hard Knocks" For the Wisest, Funniest Knitting Advice on the Web Did you know that knitting socks in China is fun because the Chinese like to flash appreciative thumbs-up signs when they see you? Or that when knitting around cats one should store balls of yarn in freezer bags to discourage playful paw swipes? Read a hysterical (and smart) collection of irreverent knitting advice from the members of **Knit List** at **http://www.benefitslink.com/knit/knitlink/hardknock.shtml**. Some typical advice: hide your nicest knitting projects from your sister whom you know will ask you to knit the same sweater for her. Now that's a good idea!

KNITTERS SHARE A SPECIAL LANGUAGE ON THE WEB

Acronyms are used widely on the Internet. Some famous ones include LOL for "laughing out loud," BTW for "by the way," and <G> for "grin." Stitchers have a few of their own. Like DH for "dear husband" and UFO for "unfinished object" (something we all have closets full of). But knitters on the Internet share a special lexicon of acronyms and code words that almost rivals in its complexity knitting abbreviations. You can find a list in the **Knit List FAQs** (**http://www.woolworks.org/faqlist.html**) and more at **Wool Works** (**http://www.woolworks.org /terms.html**). Here is a sample:

Frog—To rip out lots of stitches at once, as in the frog's refrain "rip it, rip it."
Tink—To rip stitches one at a time. Comes from "knit" spelled backwards.
KIP—Knitting in public
KB—Knitting Buddy(s)
TOAD—Trashed Object, Abandoned in Disgust
YAQ—Yarn Acquisition Quest
YCZ—Yarn Containment Zone (where one's stash is cached)
SEX—Stash Enrichment eXpedition
FOREPLAY—For Our Really Exciting Projects, Let's Add Yarn
NQBE—Not Quite Big Enough
TTFN—Ta Ta For Now

Usenet Discussion Groups

Knitters also hang out in these Usenet discussion groups:
rec.crafts.textiles.yarn
rec.crafts.textiles.misc
rec.crafts.textiles.needlework
rec.crafts.textiles.machine-knit
uk.rec.crafts

Knitting Guilds

THE KNITTING GUILD OF AMERICA
http://www.tkga.com/

You'll find complete information on joining this guild, plus links to Web sites of local chapters, and patterns to download.

KNITTING GUILDS
http://www.woolworks.org/guilds.html

Emily Way offers a comprehensive directory of knitting guilds around the United States and Canada, with e-mail and Web site links.

Knitting Software

MACHINE LIST SOFTWARE SITE
http://www.mnsinc.com/hagerty/index.html

The Web site of the Machine List discussion group for knitting machine owners offers a library of hard-to-find shareware and freeware programs for both hand and machine knitters. Some of their offerings: Mom's Knitting, which calculates gauges and dimensions; a knitting pattern database program; the Magic Formula Calculator for calculating increases and decreases; Judith Hiam's Knitnotes for calculating sweater patterns; a demo of Ileen Levy's Design-A-Pattern; plus various grid designing programs.

ARANPAINT
http://opera.iinet.net.au/~coolhoun/index.html

AranPaint is a Windows 95/98 program for designing sweaters. A demo is available.

COCHENILLE DESIGN STUDIO
http://www.cochenille.com/

© 1999 Susan Lazear

Cochenille sells numerous programs for knit design including Stitch Painter, for knit graphing on both Windows and Macs, and Garment Styler for garment shaping.

COLORKNIT FOR THE MACINTOSH
ftp.cs.tu-berlin.de/pub/mac/appl/ColorKnit:307.sit.bin

This is a simple program for graphing knits for either hand or machine knitting.

DESIGNAKNIT
http://www.knitcraft.com/designaknit.html

You can download a demo of this industrial-strength Windows program for designing knits for hand or machine knitting. Knitcraft is the importer in the United States and Canada.

KNITWARE
http://www.islandnet.com/knitware/

Janet Tombu sells a remarkable program for generating sweater patterns on PCs. She also sells a version to generate teddy bear and doll sweater patterns.

Searching for Knitters in Your Area to Penpal With?

There are a number of local e-mail knitters' mailing lists. There's one for knitters in New York, for instance, and another for knitters in Toronto. Knit List keeps a list, and you can read it at **http://www.woolworks.org/faqlist.html.**

Use Cross-stitch Software to Chart Knits

Cross-stitch graphing software is perfect for charting knits—assuming that the software lets you "elongate" the grid squares to approximate the dimensions of knit stitches. Several of the cross-stitch graphing programs do, the market leader Pattern Maker by Hobbyware (**http://www.hobbyware.com**). You can download a trial version of Pattern Maker—and many other cross-stitch programs on the Web. Head to the "Free Stuff for Cross-stitchers" chapter, starting on page 77, for more information.

Bookmark Your Favorite Web Sites

It's easy to get lost on the Web, and sometimes difficult to find your way back to a great Web site you may have visited a half hour ago—or yesterday. You can find Web sites you've previously visited by pulling down the history list in the top bar of your browser. But your browser records in that history list only URLs that you've actually typed into its location bar; in other words, it won't record URLs that you've clicked your way through to Web links. The solution is to bookmark favorite sites. To do so all you need to do is click the Bookmark button on your Web browser, or pull down the bookmark menu and select Add Bookmark. In Internet Explorer pull down the Favorites menu and click Add to Favorites.

free Stuff for Machine Knitters

Whether you churn out intarsias in semi-production fashion with a computer-driven Passap or occasionally needle a Dr. Who scarf with some obscure quasi-automated knitting frame you bought from a cable shopping channel, you'll find other knitters in cyberspace who are doing exactly the same thing. And perhaps suffering the same problems as well. You'll even find machine knitters on **America Online** (use the keyword "knitting" to find them if you're a subscriber).

As for all knitting needs the best place to find other machine knitters is the big mailing list discussion group **Knit List** (see page 50 for instructions on how to sign up). But there are other mailing lists especially for machine knitters—you can read about them in the following pages. They're wonderful places to go for help.

A large group of machine knitters hang out on the online service **CompuServe** (use the "go" word "fibercrafts" if you're a member).

On the Web you'll find machine knitters on **Delphi's Textile Arts** site (**http://www.delphi.com/textile**) run by Rita Levine.

A lot of machine knitters also hang out in the Usenet newsgroup **rec.crafts.textiles.machine-knit**.

Surf the Machine Knitter's Web Ring

Machine knitters with Web pages connect to each other through a Web ring. You don't have to "join" the ring. Instead you just click your way around it to visit various pages. You can tap in by heading to **http://members.tripod.com/~Sandy_one/machine knit.html**.

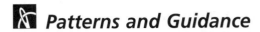 **Patterns and Guidance**

ANGELIKA'S STUDIO
http://www.ucinet.com/~angelika/

© 1999 Angelika Burles

Angelika's Web site is a machine knitter's goldmine, with lots of patterns and directions, and a free newsletter in which Angelika writes "any advice I can think of" such as discussions of which knitting machine to buy.

TINA'S KNITTING MACHINE PAGE
http://www.bit-net.com/~rpollina/knitting/

You'll find here tutorials, FAQs, a swatch database, advice on converting hand knitting patterns to machine ones, a glossary of machine terms, plus "Tina's Unofficial Guide to Bond Machines."

PRIMARILY PASSAP!
http://members.tripod.com/~wquinn/passap.html

Here's a Web site for owners of Passaps, with a terrific list of links to Internet resources for this brand of knitting machines.

MACHINE KNITTING PATTERNS
http://www.dplus.net/caramark/free.html

Cara L. Bernhauser offers instructions for machine knitting a head-band, leg warmers, and more.

BOND LIST THOUGHTS PAGE
http://www.wlv.ac.uk/~in1036/knitting/bond/list/listhint.htm

It sounds like the name of a meditation journal for a self-help group, doesn't it? The Bond list is a group of knitters who use Bond knitting machines. (In the following pages you'll learn how to join them.) This is a collection of commonly asked questions, advice, and instructions.

COLLECTED WISDOM FROM BOND LIST
http://www.southern.edu/~williams/machinek.html

Here's another collection of advice from Bond List, assembled by Clifford L. Williams.

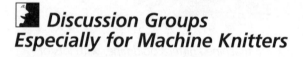

Discussion Groups
Especially for Machine Knitters

BOND KNITTERS' CLUB ONLINE
http://www.userhome.com/knittingtoday/

Tap into this Web page for directions on how to join an e-mail discussion group for owners of Bond machines, including the Classic, the Elite, the Studio, and of course the Incredible Sweater Machine.

KNITTING MACHINE CLUBS
http://www.userhome.com/knittingtoday/Clubs.htm

The Bond Knitters' Club offers a list of knitting machine clubs around the country.

SOCKS

Betty Allen runs this list for machine knitters who knit socks. To subscribe e-mail socks-request@mylist.net *with* subscribe *as the message.*

MACHINE KNITTERS' LIST WEB PAGE
http://www.mnsinc.com/hagerty/index.html

*Amy Stinson (*amys@iquest.net *or* amys@amys-answers.com*) runs three e-mail discussion groups for knitters:* **Machknit**, **Machknit-chat** *and* **DAK**. *The Machine Knitters' List (Machknit) is concerned with the technical aspect of using knitting machines, while its counterpart Machknit-chat is for socializing. The DAK list is devoted to using DesignaKnit, the high-end knitting garment design software that's used by many machine knitters. You can read more about all these groups by heading to the Machine Knitters' List Web Page. You'll also find lots of free patterns and technical advice on the Web site.*

To sign up for Machine Knit, send an e-mail message to listserv@amys-answers.com *with this in the body of the message:* subscribe machknit firstname lastname.

To sign up for Machine Knit-Chat, send an e-mail message to listserv@amys-answers.com *with this in the body of the message:* subscribe machknit-chat firstname lastname.

Software for Machine Knitters

ROSE'S KNITS
http://www.roses-knits.com/

Rose sells a variety of software to assist in the use of computerized knitting machines like the Passap. She offers free downloadable utilities and patterns.

DESIGNAKNIT
http://www.knitcraft.com/designaknit.html

DAK is the high-end knitting design program, and the one that interfaces with many computerized knitting machines. You can download a demo here (sorry, Mac fans, it's for Windows only). Knitcraft is the importer for the United States and Canada.

KNIT2FIT GARMENT SHAPING
BEACON HILL KNITS
http://www.daknews.com/

Knit2Fit is one of many DAK add-ons. There are no downloadable versions available, but Beacon Hill offers considerable resources and information for machine knitters.

COCHENILLE DESIGN STUDIO
http://www.cochenille.com/

Cochenille sells books and utilities for computerized knitting machines, including Stitch Painter for graphing knits (for both Windows and Mac), and Garment Styler for designing knit garments.

CHAPTER 4

free Stuff for Embroiderers

There's a common thread among embroiderers who hang out on the Internet (excuse the pun): All marvel at how fast their stitch and technique repertoire has grown simply by exchanging e-mail with other stitchers. It's true! Many weekend cross-stitchers have found themselves plunging off into the brave worlds of pulled thread and ribbon embroidery through the encouragement of online pals. That's probably why there are so many resources for embroiderers on the Web. Embroiderers are constantly nudging each other to try new techniques and products.

Big Embroidery Web Sites

COUNTED CROSS STITCH, NEEDLEWORK, AND STITCHERY
http://www.wco.com/%7Ekdyer/xstitch.html

The very best place to go for embroidery information and links to other resources around the Web is Kathleen M. Dyer's big Web site. She offers extensive collections and links to stitching references, "online classes," and thread charts. She also offers links to the Usenet discussion group **rec.crafts.textiles.needlework** *where lots of embroiderers hang out.*

EMBROIDERY RESOURCES AT THE WORLD WIDE ART RESOURCES
http://www.wwar.com/creator/embroidery.html

You'll find a chat room and message forum for embroiderers, plus links to very unusual embroidery information around the Internet.

TEXTILE ARTS FROM DELPHI
http://www.delphi.com/textile

Rita Levine hosts this excellent service that includes feature articles, and a chat area and bulletin boards for embroiderers and other fiber folk.

EMBROIDER THE WEB
http://members.aol.com/ecnpage/index.html

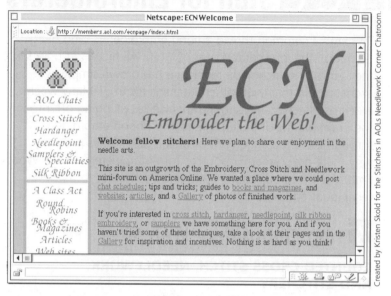

Created by Kristen Skold for the Stitchers in AOLs Needlework Corner Chatroom.

Kristen Skold created this information-packed site for the embroidery, cross-stitch, and needlework discussion groups on America Online. You don't need to be a member of AOL to tap in.

NEEDLEARTS: THE FIBER ARTS FORUM
http://needlearts.dm.net

You can read about many thread arts here—from embroidery to ribbon work. There's a bulletin board, a chat area, and free monthly patterns. Past ones include an Assisi pattern and blackwork embroidered roses.

UK SITES OF STITCHING INTEREST
http://www.aion.demon.co.uk/

This lovely site by Christine-Ann Martin in the United Kingdom includes astrological Assisi patterns, a penpal board, and links to United Kingdom stitching magazines.

NEEDLEWORK FROM MARTHA BETH LEWIS
http://www.serve.com/marbeth/needlework.html

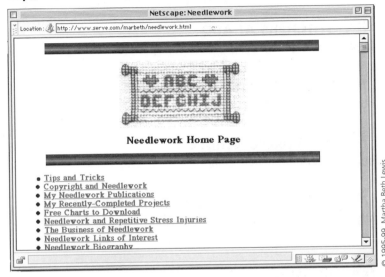

© 1995-99, Martha Beth Lewis

Martha Beth Lewis offers a great resource for stitchers, including tips and tricks, free patterns, and information on copyrights.

 ## CLASSIC STITCHES ON THE WEB
http://www.classicstitches.com/

 ## *Free Charts*

These sites offer an ever-changing roster of free embroidery charts, as well as tips and tutorials.

 ## NEEDLECRAFT SHOWCASE FREE AREA
http://www.stitching.com/freestuff

Stitching tips, a bulletin board, free patterns, and a chat area are part of the fun here.

Learn About Preserving Your Embroidery

Head to the Web site of **Archival Products** (**http://www.archival.com**) and click on *Newsletter* for advice on preserving paper, photographs, and textiles.

COATES AND CLARK
http://www.coatsandclark.com/index.htm

STITCHERS AT ABQ
http://www.highfiber.com/~stitcher/freepatterns.html

WONDERFUL STITCHES WWW
http://www.needlework.com/

THE NORDIC NEEDLE
http://www.nordicneedle.com/

NOSTALGIA NEEDLEWORK HOME PAGE
http://www.nostalgianeedlework.com/

Lessons

CARON COLLECTION'S DYED AND GONE TO HEAVEN
http://www.caron-net.com/

This site's a treasure with a wide-ranging collection of online lessons including "Using Variegated Threads for Dramatic Effects," "Fun with the Woven Stitch," and "Tenerife Embroidery."

STITCHING WITH SILK, FROM KREINIK
http://www.kreinik.com/educate.htm

For links to more embroidery resources around the Internet head to **Cynthia Chesler's Cyberstitch Embroidery Links** (**http://cyberstitch.hypermart.net/guide/embroidery.htm**).

🛒 HARDANGER LESSONS FROM NORDIC NEEDLE BY SUSAN MEIER AND ROSALYN WATNEMO

http://www.nordicneedle.com/listing.htm

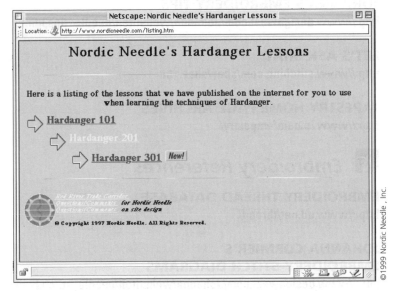

©1999 Nordic Needle, Inc.

"SHISHA MIRROR EMBROIDERY" BY SHAKTI

http://www.his.com/~jdalexa/v_d/shisha.html

🛒 "ALL ABOUT GOLD THREADS" BY W. S. K. BARNES, MANAGING DIRECTOR OF BENSON & JOHNSON, LTD. OF LONDON

http://www.needlearts.com/ega/article/october.html

🔏 *Collected Embroidery Wisdom*

THE REC.CRAFTS.TEXTILES.NEEDLEWORK FAQ'S

The most wonderful collection of stitching "wisdom" collected on the Net are the FAQ files from the Usenet newsgroup **rec.crafts. textiles.needlework**. *They span every stitching subject imaginable, from how to select threads, to how to care for needlework, and how to find out-of-print patterns. You can read the whole collection by tapping into rec.crafts.textiles.needlework or by heading to Kathleen Dyer's Web site* (**http://www.wco.com/%7Ekdyer/faq.html**).

FRAN'S STITCHING TIPS
http://www.tomtr.com/tip.html

JOHANNA'S EMBROIDERY TIPS
http://www.designwest.com/Johanna/webstitch/needle_tips.html

LET'S ASK SHAY
http://www.stitching.com/shay/shay.htm

TAPESTRY HOME PAGE ARCHIVES
http://www.io.com/~tapestry/

 Embroidery References

EMBROIDERY THREAD DATABASE
http://www.ud.net/thread/

JOHANNA CORMIER'S
EMBROIDERY STITCH DIAGRAMS
http://www.designwest.com/Johanna/webstitch/needle_stitch.html

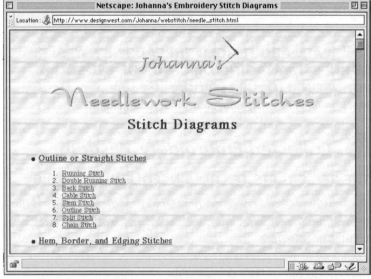

SHARON BOGGON'S NEEDLEWORK STITCH DICTIONARY

http://online.anu.edu.au/english/jems/sharon/stitchdictionary
contents.html

©1999 Sharon Boggon

"DICTIONARY OF EMBROIDERY TERMS" BY MICHAEL SANDERSON IN FRANCE

http://www.island.net/~stitch/glossary.html

SILK RIBBON EMBROIDERY STITCH DICTIONARY

http://www.ribbonworks.com/stitch/stitch.html

"THREAD FACTS" BY ROSE MARIE TONDL AND WENDY RICH FROM THE UNIVERSITY OF NEBRASKA-LINCOLN

http://www.ianr.unl.edu/pubs/NebFacts/NF37.HTM

A PRIMER ON EMBROIDERY NEEDLES

http://www.stitching.com/needle.htm

A GUIDE TO RIBBON EMBROIDERY STITCHES FROM THE CHARTED DESIGNERS OF AMERICA
http://www.stitching.com/CDA/Ribbon.htm

"WASHING EMBROIDERED GARMENTS" FROM MADERIA USA THREADS
http://www.concentric.net/~Madusa/sx060005.htm

INTERNATIONAL TAPESTRY NETWORK
http://www.alaska.net/~itnet/

Web Sites of Embroidery Thread Manufacturers

These are the Web sites of major thread manufacturers who offer neat things for embroiderers, including thread charts, care guides, tips, features on techniques, and even online magazines. You can find a complete list of thread manufacturers' Web sites at **Kathleen Dyer's** Web site (**http://www.wco.com /%7Ekdyer/manufact.html**).

KREINIK MANUFACTURING
http://www.kreinik.com/index.html

EDMAR RAYON THREADS (MAKERS OF THREAD FOR BRAZILIAN EMBROIDERY)
http://www.edmar-co.com/rayon.htm

MADERIA USA THREADS
http://www.concentric.net/~Madusa/

DMC USA
http://www.dmc-usa.com/

GINNIE THOMPSON, THE FLOWER THREAD PEOPLE
http://www.flowerthread.com/

CARON THREADS' NEEDLEPOINT, CROSS-STITCH, AND OTHER NEEDLEWORK AND THREAD RESOURCES
http://www.caron-net.com/

©1999 Lois Caron

 Embroidery Magazines

STITCH ON LINE: A MAGAZINE OF EMBROIDERY AND OTHER NEEDLECRAFT, PAST, PRESENT AND FUTURE
http://ourworld.compuserve.com/homepages/textile_gallery/

This is a wonderful little "ezine" from the Skinner sisters with articles and source lists on topics like blackwork embroidery.

THE WORLD OF EMBROIDERY
http://www.hiraeth.com/world-emb/

Published in London by the Embroiderer's Guild, this site includes full-length articles on intriguing subjects like the "exciting effects of using polymer clay with machine embroidery."

CLASSIC STITCHES
http://www.classicstitches.com/

You need to type your name and address into this site in order to access free charts and tutorials from this Scottish embroidery magazine.

THE NEEDLEARTS MALL ARTICLES OF THE MONTH
http://www.needlearts.com/articles/articles.html

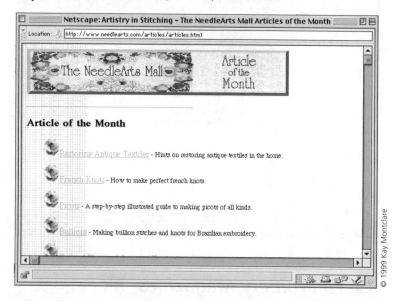

When Gloria was a teen she subscribed to Kay Montclare's Hands On *and eagerly anticipated each month lesson kits that consisted of thread and instructions for a new stitch. (Her friends scoffed, "That stuff sure looks like it will lead to an exciting career." Little did they know.) Imagine her delight when she found many of those cherished articles and lessons on this extraordinary Web site! You can read about bullion knots, Brazilian embroidery, twisted floss, metal threads, and more. Bookmark this site!*

SILK RIBBON TALK
http://www.ribbonworks.com/newslett/newslet.html

EMBROIDERY BUSINESS NEWS
http://www.ebnmag.com/

THE NEEDLEWORKER MAGAZINE
http://www.needleworker.com/

✕ Historical and International Embroidery Sites

THE BRANWELL/BRONTE SAMPLERS
http://www2.sbbs.se/hp/cfalk/sampler.htm

Lori Bell tells about samplers that the Bronte sisters stitched.

BLACKWORK EMBROIDERY ARCHIVES
www.pobox.com/~pkm/bwarch.html   *www.blackworkarchives.com*

Elizabethan Blackwork fanatics, let us introduce you to heaven. Paula Katherine Marmor presents patterns, information, and an excellent how-to on the double-running stitch.

Join a Round Robin

What's a "round robin?" A stitcher will stitch part of a sampler and mail it to another stitcher. The second stitcher will stitch her unique design on it, then mail it to another stitcher. And so on. There are often dozens of round robins going on at any given time in cyberspace. You can join a band sampler round robin by heading to Deborah McMahon's **Band Sampler Round Robins Web Site (http://NeedleworkSamplers.com/Round_Robins/)**.

THE BAYEUX TAPESTRY
http://blah.bsuvc.bsu.edu/bt

View sections of the complete tapestry, plus close-ups of stitching details (some are rather bawdy).

2BUSY STITCHING: HISTORY LESSONS
http://www.2busystitching.com/book.htm

Read the history of embroidery while learning a variety of stitches.

CATHERINE DECKER'S JACOBEAN EMBROIDERY PAGE
http://locutus.ucr.edu/~cathy/craft.html

CHINESE CULTURE IN TAIWAN: EMBROIDERY
http://www.houstoncul.org/culdir/embr/embr.htm

This site, sponsored by China's Ministry of Education discusses embroidery throughout Chinese history.

CHINESE TEXTILES, ONE THOUSAND YEARS
http://www.asianart.com/textiles/textile.html

The Urban Council and Hong Kong Museum of Art highlight pieces from their exhibit.

HUNAN EMBROIDERY
http://www.hunanembroidery.com/

THE JAPANESE EMBROIDERY CENTER
http://www.japaneseembroidery.com/

Located in Georgia, and founded in 1989 by Shuji and Masa Tamura, this nonprofit organization's mission is to preserve and promote the cultural heritage of traditional Japanese embroidery.

MEDIEVAL EMBROIDERY PAGE
FROM MASTER RICHARD WYMARC'S
http://ourworld.compuserve.com/homepages/Wymarc/master1.htm

Timothy J. Mitchell presents historical embroidery for the modern era.

MEDIEVAL/RENAISSANCE EMBROIDERY HOMEPAGE
http://www.staff.uiuc.edu/~jscole/medembro.html

JAPANESE EMBROIDERY HOME PAGE
http://www.gate.net/~aubin/

VICTORIANA LIBRARY, "SOUTHERN DECORATIVE NEEDLEWORK" BY HEATHER PALMER
http://www.victoriana.com/library/south.html

MACEDONIAN FOLK EMBROIDERY
http://www.auburn.edu/academic/liberal_arts/foreign/macedonia/folk-embroidery/index.html

Maintained by George Mitrevski from Auburn University, this site contains beautiful examples of Macedonia Folk Embroidery

Free Clipart for Spinners, Weavers, and Knitters
Straw Into Gold (**http://www.straw.com/clipart/**) offers a collection of free clipart featuring pictures of spinners, spinning wheels, sheep and cotton that fiber fans can use on their personal Web pages.

THE VICTORIAN LIBRARY—19TH CENTURY SAMPLER COLLECTION
http://www.victoriana.com/archive/jacobs.html

See eight nineteenth-century samplers, all embroidered by a young girl: Elizabeth E. Jacobs from Long Stowe, England.

TAPESTRIES FROM GALERIE BLONDEEL-DEROYAN—PARIS
http://www.franceantiq.fr/sna/blonder/

View extraordinary antique tapestries from this Paris collection.

Embroidery Discussions

You can find other embroiderers on **America Online** in the Needlework forum (use the keyword "crafts"). You'll also find embroiderers in **Woman's Day Online** on AOL (use the keywords "woman's day" and once you're in the magazine area head to the Craft Corner).

CompuServe hosts avid stitchers in its Fibercrafts Forum (use the go word "fibercrafts").

But you'll find even more embroiders in the Usenet newsgroups:

rec.crafts.textiles.needlework
rec.crafts.textiles.misc
uk.rec.craft

You can tap in through **DejaNews** (http://www.dejanews .com) or **Kathleen Dyer's** Web page (http://www.wco.com /%7Ekdyer /rctn.html).

Looking for a few stitchers to chat with? Try out the **#Stitch IRC Cannel**. For more information head to the channel's home page (**http://www.net1plus.com/users/sissy/ircStitch.html**).

 *Mailing Lists*

HISTORICAL NEEDLEWORK
Discuss the techniques used in antique needlework by signing up for this mailing list. Send an e-mail message to: majordomo@ansteorra.org. In the body of the message write: *subscrib h-needlework*

SILK RIBBON EMBROIDERY
http://www.jps.net/hydearts/silklist.html

Beth-Katherine Kaiman invites you to join her list at Garden Fairies and tells you how at this page.

 Bulletin Boards and Chat Rooms

These sites include very active embroidery bulletin boards, and in some cases chat rooms too.

EMBROIDERY.COM
http://www.embroidery.com/

2BUSY STITCHING
http://www.2busystitching.com/

WONDERFUL STITCHES: CELEBRATING DECORATIVE STITCH IN NEEDLEPOINT AND CROSS-STITCH
http://www.needlework.com/

Embroidery Guilds and Other Organizations

THE EMBROIDERER'S GUILD OF AMERICA
http://www.needlearts.com/ega/

EMBROIDERY GUILDS OF AUSTRALIA
http://www.geko.net.au/~fthorne/craft/guilds.html

EMBROIDERS' ASSOCIATION OF CANADA, INC.
http://www.eac.ca/embroidery/

THE NATIONAL ACADEMY OF NEEDLEARTS
http://www.needleart.org

THE NATIONAL NEEDLEWORK ASSOCIATION
http://www.creative-industries.com/tnna

THE ROYAL SCHOOL OF NEEDLEWORK
http://www.needleart.org

NATIONAL EMBROIDERY TEACHER'S ASSOCIATION
e-mail **suekerndt@juno.com** for information on joining.

Send a Greeting to an Online Penpal

At the **Stitchers' Virtual Greeting Card**
(**http://NeedleworkSamplers.com/Stitchers_Cards/index.shtml**)
you can send a free card to a friend. Or, try **AdOnWeb's
Envirocards** (**http://www.adonweb.com/cards/index.html**).
Cards can include animation and sound.

Join WARP to "Weave a Real Peace"
WARP is a group of fiber art activists on the Web
who work to promote through textile arts the
self-empowerment and betterment of women and
impoverished communities throughout the world.
To read more about this fascinating group head to
http:w3.thegroup.net/~janis/warp.html

CHAPTER 5

free Stuff for Cross-Stitchers

Cross-stitch ranks with knitting as one of the most soothing needlearts. Years ago, when Judy, then afraid of flying, quaked at the prospect of a business trip, she spotted a cross-stitched picture in a store window and knew immediately that all the fastidiousness that such an art required would tranquilize her while rocketing four thousand feet above the ground. And indeed it did (along with a purse-sized bottle of scotch). She traversed the country several times in comfort, although the floss ended up tangled and the stitches weren't terribly straight. She eventually concluded that for maximum flying ease one should pack the most complex stitch chart available (75 floss colors minimum), and chug two daiquiris in the airport bar before staggering onto the plane and starting it. Maybe *you* cross-stitch in front of your computer because it makes computer use less traumatic (Judy does that too). If so, you'll find many other stitchers on the Web who rely on stitching to get them through bumpy patches in their day. You'll also find lots of free advice and patterns—many complex enough to carry on a dreaded flight.

 You'll find more cross-stitch friendly Web sites in the Free Stuff for Embroiderers chapter, starting on page 61.

Travel Web Rings to Visit the Web Pages of Cross-Stitchers

You can click your way from one cross-stitch page to another by tapping into a ring, or group of inter-linked pages. Head to the **Cross-Stitcher's Web Ring** (**http://www.yellowline.com/cross-stitcher/ring.shtml**) or the **Evenweave Fabricstabber Web Ring** (**http://www.dm.net/~marg/evenweave.htm**). You don't have to join the ring to travel it—just click on its icon.

Big Cross-Stitch Web Sites

These Web sites are the best places to go on the Web to get started looking for cross-stitch help and information.

KATHY DYER'S COUNTED CROSS STITCH, NEEDLEWORK, AND STITCHERY PAGE
http://www.ncal.verio.com/~kdyer/xstitch.html

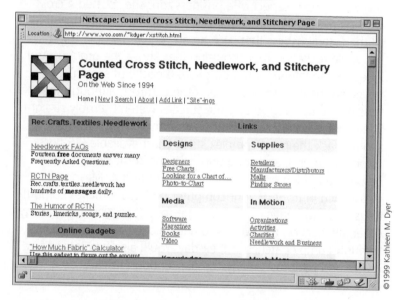

©1999 Kathleen M. Dyer

Kathy's vast site answers just about every question you have about cross-stitch—and other needlearts. It also serves as portal to just about everything of importance on the Web. She also offers FAQs and information about Usenet newsgroup needleart discussions.

CROSS STITCHING FROM THE MINING CO.
http://crossstitch.miningco.com

Meridel L. Abrams is the host of this wonderful resource for stitchers. You'll find regular feature stories (most written by Abrams), links to other stitching information on the Web, online chats, a bulletin board for cross-stitchers, and much more.

CAMEOROZE'S CROSS-STITCH STUDIO
http://www.nidlink.com/~ddavaz/margaret/studio/studio.html

Margaret Davaz runs a great Web site for stitchers with links to all the best cross-stitch stuff on the Web.

 # Free Charts

Get PCStitch's Pattern Viewer to Print Cross-stitch Patterns

To view and print patterns on some of these sites you'll need to download a copy of PCStitch's free Pattern Viewer, available for both PCs and Macs (**http://www.pcstitch.com**). You'll know that a pattern has been stored in the special PCStitch format if it has a .PAT extension at the ends of its name. For patterns stored in other graphics formats, head to Chapter 1 for directions on storing and printing them.

Many cross-stitch designers, both amateur and professional, offer free patterns on their Web sites. There are more than we could possibly chronicle, so here are just a few of our favorites.

TIPS FROM TERESA! BY TERESA WENTZLER
http://www.infostudio.com/TW/Resources/Tips/index.html

Chart designer Wentzler shares tips on everything from specialty stitches to keeping your projects organized. She even runs a bulletin board where fans of her patterns can chat with her.

 ### DRAGON DREAMS FREEBIES
http://DragonDreams.accra.ca/free.html

Dragon Lady, Jennifer Aikman-Smith, shares a dragon-of-the-month cross-stitch pattern. She offers patterns of angels and other mythical creatures as well.

MARILYN LEAVITT-IMBLUM'S CHRISTMAS ANGELS
http://www.tiag.com/

Marilyn Leavitt-Imblum of Told in a Garden, Lavender & Lace, and Butternut Road fame, shares her annual Christmas angel patterns. These are the patterns you can pick up free in cross-stitch stores in December, but if you missed a year they're all available to download.

DMC PROJECT ARCHIVE
http://www.dmc-usa.com/projects/archive/archive.html

Thread maker DMC offers an extensive library of free patterns. You'll need PCStitch's Pattern Viewer to print them.

🛒 C.M. BARR'S
COUNTED CROSS STITCH DESIGNS
http://www.barrs.simplenet.com/fc/design1.html

Barr offers some of her original patterns for you to download, including some great cat ones.

FREE TOOLS AND PATTERNS FOR CROSS STITCHERS
http://www.burtlake.com/stitch/patterns.htm

Carrie Luhmann offers a bunch of free charts, plus advice on washing fabric.

🛒 NEEDLE NECESSITIES FREE PATTERNS
http://www.needlenecessities.com/patterns.html

Needle Necessities offers new free patterns every month.

🛒 JULIE OLIVER'S CROSS-STITCH PATTERNS
http://ausmall.com.au/oztralia/sample.htm

Julie offers a free pattern of a koala in a gumtree, and more.

DONNA VERMILLION GIAMPA'S STITCHERY
http://www.vsccs.com

Donna designs some of the most beautiful cross-stitch patterns found in kits and magazines. On her Web site she shares free patterns—and design advice. A super-neat site!

COUTURE'S CROSS-STITCH PAGE
http://members.aol.com/cdcouture/homepage/page_1.html

Cynthia Denise Couture has assembled extensive free patterns.

©1999 The Vermillion Stitchery

◻ JENNY RASMUSSEN'S CROSS-STITCH PATTERNS

http://www.mindspring.com/~roadrunner1/CrossStitch/CrossStitch.html

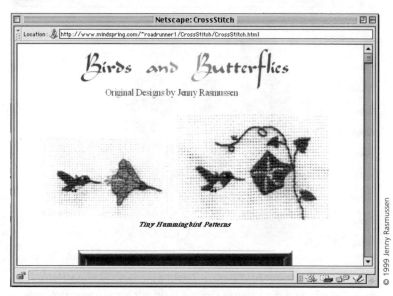

© 1999 Jenny Rasmussen

Jenny offers free nature-inspired patterns of her own design, including many that bird-lovers will enjoy.

ZWEIGART
http://www.zweigart.com

Fabric maker Zweigart offers a variety of free charts from well-known designers.

◼ *The charts that these Web sites offer are for personal and not commercial use. Please respect the copyrights of the designers who so generously make them available and do not produce the designs for sale.*

 Free How-Tos

Usenet Needlecraft FAQs

One of the best collections of advice for cross-stitchers—and other needlecrafters as well, is assembled in the frequently asked question files for the Usenet newsgroup **rec.crafts.textiles.needlework**. There are presently over a dozen. Topics include: Needlework activities; books and videos; competitions, selling needlework; software; cross-stitch tutorial; making your own cross-stitch charts; designers; fabric information; information on threads, fibers, and embellishments; magazines; manufacturers and distributors; organizations; retailers; stitching and embroidery techniques. Some of the FAQ's are updated monthly, some weekly.

Kathleen Dyer is the head editor and librarian (an immense job!). You can find links to the FAQ's on her Web site (**http://www.wco.com/~kdyer/documents/how_to_get_faq.html**). When you read them drop Kathy a note of thanks for maintaining this rich and wonderful resource.

"DMC TO ANCHOR FLOSS CONVERSION CHART" FROM THE YARN TREE
http://yarntree.com/019dmccn.htm

"FROM FLOWER TO TEXTILE, THE STORY OF LINEN" FORM LIBECO LAGAE
http://www.libeco.be/eng/consumer/fr_pros.htm

"HOW MUCH FABRIC CALCULATOR" FROM KATHY DYER
http://www.ncal.verio.com/~kdyer/cgi-bin/fabric_size.cgi

"LEARN CROSS-STITCH IN FIVE MINUTES" FROM THE YARN TREE
http://yarntree.com/007begin.htm

🛒 "NEEDLECRAFT HOW TO..."
FROM NEEDLECRAFT OF IRELAND
http://www.ils.ie/needlecraft/nc-howto.html

🛒 "NEEDLEPOINT AND CROSS STITCH TIPS
AND BLOCKING INSTRUCTIONS"
FROM CRAFTS NEEDLEPOINT HEIRLOOMS
http://needlepointfun.com/learn.htm

🅰 *Web Sites of Major Floss Makers*

You'll find on most of these sites guides to thread numbers, lists of retailers who carry particular thread lines, and tips and patterns.

DYED AND GONE TO HEAVEN:
AN ONLINE MAGAZINE
http://www.caron-net.com

Caron, makers of specialty threads, publishes this wonderful virtual magazine that features stitching guides and free patterns, online classes, tips, a stitcher's chat feature, and much more.

DMC FLOSS COLORS
http://www.dmc-usa.com

MADEIRA THREADS
http://www.madeirathreads.com

COATS & CLARK
http://www.coatsandclark.com

KREINIK
http://www.kreinik.com

CARON COLLECTION
http://www.caron-net.com

 Cross-Stitch Magazines

CHRIS O'DONNELL'S "COUNTED CROSS STITCH MAGAZINES LIST"
http://people.delphi.com/chrisod/mag.htm

Web Sites of Leading Cross-Stitch Magazines 🛒

Many of these magazines offer free charts, tutorials, tips, and even articles from past and current issues to read online.

BETTER HOMES & GARDENS CROSS-STITCH & NEEDLEWORK
http://www.bhglive.com/crafts/csn/csn.html

CROSS COUNTRY STITCHING
http://www.crosscountryshopping.com/magazine.htm

THE NEEDLEWORKER MAGAZINE
http://www.needleworker.com

CROSS-STITCH GALLERY
http://www.cross-x-stitch.com/csg/index.htm

THE CROSS-STITCHER
http://www.thecrossstitcher.com

STONEY CREEK CROSS STITCH COLLECTION MAGAZINE
http://www.stoneycreek.com/magazine.html

How to Find an Out of Print or Otherwise Hard to Find Pattern or Book on the Web

"Can I find a back issue of a cross-stitch magazine or an out-of-print chart on the Web?" is one of the most frequent questions stitchers ask. Yes, you can. But it may take a bit of work. Here are some tips for searching. Many are applicable to not only cross-stitch charts and magazines, but other needlework patterns and books as well. We've had great success finding books and patterns through all these sites, so we recommend them wholeheartedly.

Try Hard-to-Find Needlework Books **(http://www.needleworkbooks.com/)** Bette S. Feinstein has a huge collection of magazines and patterns going back to the 1900s, including *Needlewoman, Needle Arts—EGA, Needle & Thread*, and *Embroidery Magazine-UK*. Visit her Web site or e-mail hardtofind@needleworkbooks.com

Try Bibliofind **(http://bibliofind.com/)** You've probably heard people say you can find out-of-print books on Amazon.Com (http://www.amazon.com). But that service isn't anything compared to this one. Bibliofind searches the

Cross-Stitch Guilds

CHARTED DESIGNERS OF AMERICA
http://www.stitching.com/CDA/index.html

THE CROSS STITCH GUILD
http://www.greenoff.co.uk/coming.htm

Cross-Stitch Discussions

Cross-stitchers are a sociable bunch and you'll find them on America Online, CompuServe and Microsoft Network.

On **America Online** head to the Needlework forum (use the keyword "crafts"). You'll also find embroiderers in **Woman's Day Online** on AOL (use the keywords "woman's day" and once you're in the magazine area head to the Craft Corner).

If you're not on AOL, you can still find out what AOL stitchers are up to by visiting their Web page **AOL's Embroider the Web** (http://members.aol.com/ecnpage/index.html).

catalogs of used book dealers around the country and within seconds comes up with hard-to-find titles. Prices tend to be reasonable too.

● *Try Web Auction Sites Like eBay* (http://www.ebay.com) You'll find thousands of patterns, including old knitting and crochet ones, and also cross-stitch charts, books, and magazines on the Web auction sites. The trick is to check these sites nightly because items for sale change so fast.

● *Head to the Mining Co.* (http://www.miningco.com) *Special Interest Needlework Pages.* You'll find the latest how-to-search-for-pattern links and advice on many of the Mining Co.'s needlework pages. Meridel L. Abrams offers realms of links and good-advice on her cross-stitch pages (**http://crossstitch.mining.co.com**). Click "Pattern Searchers" for her newest list of links.

● *Check Barb's Index of Cross-Stitch* (**http://www.barbsindex.com**). Barb keeps a database of addresses of designers, distributors, and suppliers of different patterns.

● *Subscribe to The Pattern Connection* (**http://www .onecom .com/zandzcrafters**). This is a for-pay magazine for cross-stitchers searching for charts.

Stitchers hang out in **CompuServe's** Fibercrafts Forum (use the go word "fibercrafts").

Usenet's rec.crafts.textiles.needlework newsgroup is another favorite haunt of cross-stitchers. Tap in with your browser's newsreader or by heading to **Dejanews** (**http://www.dejanews.com**). Before you do you should read all about the group including all its netiquettes by heading to **Kathy Dyer's** Web site (**http://www.ncal.verio.com/~kdyer/xstitch.html**).

Regulars in the newsgroup run a number of mailing list "support groups" for those who are stitching big cross-stitch charts, like Marilyn Leavitt-Imblum's angels. Current support groups include ones for charts by Teresa Wentzler, Nora Corbett (Mirabilia), Paula Vaughn, and Darlene O'Steen. But there are many others. You can find out how to join these e-mail based groups by clicking the "Support Page" on Kathy's site, or tapping into **rec.crafts.textiles.needlework**.

Cross-Stitch Mailing Lists

MONICA SUDDS' XSTITCH

E-mail majordomo@UserHome.com *with* subscribe xstitch *or* subscribe xstitch-digest *as the message.*

CROSS-STITCHER
http://www.yellowline.com/cross-stitcher/faq.shtml
http://www.yellowline.com/cross-stitcher/index.html

E-mail majordomo@list.sirius.com *with* subscribe cross-stitcher *as the message.*

CROSSSTITCH.COM
http://www.CrossStitch.com

Write TheThread@lists.cross-stitch.com *with* subscribe *in the subject field.*

COUNTEDTHREADS

*Head to OneList (***http://www.onelist.com***) and search in the Crafts section. Write to* Domco2@aol.com *for more information.*

Turn Words Into Cross-Stitch Letters

At **CrossStitch.com (http://www.crosstitch.com)** you can enter phrases or names and the Web site will chart it in the style and size of letters you choose.

Cross-Stitch Bulletin Boards

You'll find bulletin-board style discussions on cross-stitch on these Web sites.

WONDERFUL STITCHES
http://www.needlework.com/

CROSS-STITCH MESSAGE BOARD
http://www.InsideTheWeb.com/mbs.cgi/mb125005

FOR THE LOVE OF STITCHING
http://www.InsideTheWeb.com/messageboard/mbs.cgi/mb91305

INSIDE THE WEB BULLETIN BOARDS
Round Robin Central
http://www.InsideTheWeb.com/messageboard/mbs.cgi/mb91560

THE YARN TREE'S STITCHERS MESSAGE BOARD
http://yarntree.com/024gbook.htm

 Cross-Stitch Chats

Internet chat isn't just for pimply teens searching for a cyber-date. Cross-stitchers regularly gab in chat rooms. Cross-stitchers on AOL are avid chatters. There's also a chat channel devoted to cross-stitch called **#Stitch**. Margaret Davaz, former host of the AOL chats, offers lots advice on tapping into various chat rooms at her Web site **CameoRoze's Cross-Stitch Studio** (**http://www.nidlink.com/~ddavaz/margaret/studio/studio.html**). Click "Internet Chats" for a list of cross-stitch chats, links, and directions. You can also head to **Helen's** Web page (**http://www .staff.uiuc.edu/~hmardis/irc.html**) for information about #Stitch.

 **Cross-Stitch Software**

Many of these software companies offer try-before-you-buy versions of their programs that you can download from their Web sites. Some do not. But these manufacturers are constantly changing their offerings on the Web, so we've included all major cross-stitch software makers.

CROSS-STITCH DESIGNER & LACE DESIGNER BY IL-SOFT
http://www.ilsoft.co.uk/

British software-maker IL-Soft offers several cross-stitch design programs. You can download a demo of the Windows version. A Mac version can be purchased.

CROSS-STITCH ORGANIZER BY SUSTAINABLE SYSTEMS
http://www.sustainablepc.com/Organizer.htm

A PC program for organizing your floss charts and projects.

T I P

Join a Round Robin

A round robin is when a group of stitchers get together and pass around a sampler for each to work on. Round robins are a favorite pasttime of stitchers on the Internet. Stitchers in **rec.crafts.textiles.needlework** organize a number of round robins, and you can find out about them by tapping into that newsgroup. Stitchers on AOL and Compuserve also organize round robins. To find out more tap into Helen's **Cross-Stitch Round Robin** (**http://www.staff.uiuc.edu/~hmardis /rr-info.html**) or Rosemary I.H.Powell's **Band Sampler Round Robin Page** (**http://www.netlink.co.uk/users/dozyrosy /roundrob/**). Theresa Venette also offers explanations of round robin netiquettes and procedures (**http://www.winonanet.com/ mktplace/tvenette/robin.html**).

"COUNTED CROSS STITCH SOFTWARE LIST" BY CHRIS O'DONNELL

http://people.delphi.com/chrisod/software.htm

Chris offers a comprehensive list of cross-stitch software available on the Web.

COMPUCRAFTS' CHART GENERATING PROGRAMS

http://www.islandnet.com/%7Earogers/software.html

Stitch Craft Gold, Stitch Crafts, Stitch Grapher Plus are professional chart generating programs for Windows and Macintosh. Demo available for Windows.

CROSS-STITCH PROFESSIONAL FOR WINDOWS

http://www.stitches.co.uk/stitches.htm

A PC program from DP Software, downloadable demo available.

MAGICSTITCH BY SOFTART ASSOCIATES

http://www.magicstitch.com/

Download a free demo of this charting program for PCs.

PATTERN MAKER BY HOBBYWARE, INC.
http://www.hobbyware.com/

Pattern Maker is Windows software for charting cross-stitch. You can download a demo version. (This by the way is our favorite chart-generating program.)

PCSTITCH & PCVIEWER BY M&R TECHNOLOGIES
http://www.pcstitch.com

Download a free copy of PCViewer, and take a look at PCStitch, the chart-generating program. M&R also offers an ever-changing selection of free charts.

PIXELSTITCH BY MASTERSTITCH DESIGNS
http://www.masterstitch.com

Download a demo version of this PC program to convert photos to charts.

PRO-STITCH FOR CROSS-STITCH DESIGN
http://www.rmdinc.net/software.html

Download a demo of Seeker Software's chart design software for PCs and Macs.

STITCHCRAFT BY CRAFTED SOFTWARE
http://www.pnc.com.au/~stitch

StitchCraft is a chart design program for PCs. You can download a free chart and viewer.

Looking for a Store in Your Area?

Several Web sites offer directories of local retailers. Thread-maker Caron offers a database of stores that carry their often hard-to-find threads (**http://www.caron-net.com/ordrshop.html**). You'll also find a store directory at the **Yarn Tree** (**http://yarntree.com/010store.htm**).

WIN-STITCH BY WIN-STITCH
http://www.win-stitch.com

You can download a demo of this chart design program for PCs, plus free charts.

Turn Photos into Cross-Stitch Charts?

Can you turn a family photo into a cross-stitch chart with any of the free charting programs you can download off the Web? Yes, and no. Some of the demo versions of these cross-stitch charting programs will turn a simple image into a simple chart, but for a more detailed—and bigger chart (in other words, one with nice facial detail) you need to buy the commercial version of these programs. There are also a number of Web sites that will turn a photo into a chart for you for a fee like $30-$40. These are good deals we think, especially if you plan to chart just one family photo. A service that we like is **Beverly Crider's Custom Stitches (http://www.sustainablepc.com/Stitches.htm)**.

CHAPTER 6

free Stuff for Needlepointers

Cokie Roberts, the TV political commentator, says that as she stabs her needle through a needlepoint canvas during network meetings, men watch her warily as if she's Madame Defarge. Erma Bombeck used to say that her favorite way to spend an evening was to needlepoint herself silly in front of the TV, her husband on the couch beside her. Needlepointers are a bold and creative bunch. They include maverick designers like **Kaffee Fassett (http://www.uta.fi/opiskelu/fassett/index.html)** who see the world in riveting strokes of color and painterly fields of stitches. But the strange thing about needlepoint is that it seems to slip in and out of fashion with the fervency of a political movement. At times it's darn hard to find great patterns, canvases, and of course decent wool threads. But they're out there on the Internet, along with other needlepointers.

Finding Other Needlepointers on the Web

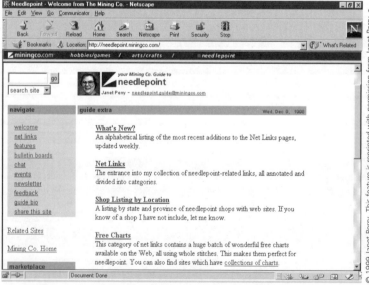

© 1999 Janet Perry. This feature is reprinted with permission from Janet Perry, a Guide at the Miningco.com, Inc. The Miningco.com, Inc. can be found on the Web atm www.Miningco.com. To follow this series online at Janet's site on Needlepoint go to needlepoint.miningco.com.

The best place to start your hunt is Janet Perry's **Needlepoint at The Mining Company (http://needlepoint.miningco.com/)**. Janet offers regular features on needlepoint, a newsletter, and the Web's best list of ever-changing free needlepoint pattern offerings on the Web. She tells you where to find free charts for animals, flowers, and even Celtic designs. There's also a bulletin board and chat area where needlepointers can commune.

You'll also find a lot of needlepointers in the Usenet discussion groups **rec.crafts.textiles.needlework** and the United Kingdom-focused **uk.rec.crafts**. You can access both through your Web browser (see Chapter 1) or by heading to the newsgroup service **DejaNews (http://www.dejanews.com)**.

Some of the textile-themed Web sites—like **Diana Lane's Textiles.Org (http://www.textiles.org)** and **Delphi's Textile Arts (http://www.delphi.com/textile)**—are also good resources for needlepointers.

Needlepoint Magazines

DYED AND GONE TO HEAVEN
http://www.caron-net.com/

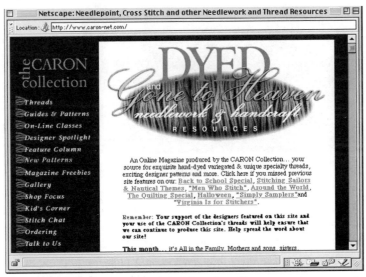

© 1999 Lois Caron

Caron, manufacturer of specialty threads, offers an online magazine that includes free charts for needlepoint, plus stitch guides, tips, a stitcher's chat area, and other freebies.

H a p p y   H o l i d a y s

Last-minute holiday shopping? eBay's Gift Alert will save the day!

Help children, and get unique holiday gifts at the Toys for Tots charity auctions.

Large Needlepoint Tapestry Pattern Canvas PIC
Item #46969997

Collectibles:Crafts:Supplies:General

Description	Currently	**$9.99**	First bid	$9.99
	Quantity	1	# of bids	1 (bid history) (with emails)
	Time left	**2 days, 14 hours +**	Location	**Calif 93725**
	Started	12/04/98 14:20:48 PST	✉ (mail this auction to a friend)	
	Ends	12/11/98 14:20:48 PST	🔔 (request a gift alert) NEW!	
Bid!	Seller	thunderdog (146) ☆		
		(view seller's feedback) (view seller's other auctions) (ask seller a question)		
	High bid	confranfan (19) ☆		
	Payment	Money Order/Cashiers Checks, Personal Checks		
	Shipping	Buyer pays actual shipping charges, Seller ships internationally		

Seller assumes all responsibility for listing this item. You should contact the seller to resolve any questions before bidding. Currency is U.S. dollars (US$) unless otherwise noted.

Description

Rico-Gobelin #59749 "Alpensee" 50/70, made in W. Germany 100% cotton. The scene is an Alpine cabin on a lake--the image size is 27.5" x 19". The total canvas is 33.5" x 25.5". Three edges are secured with duct tape and the top is attached to a wooden dowel. This canvas is ready to start working--but nothing more than those preparations noted have been done. Color numbers are keyed to colors in the pattern along the right side--there are 28 colors in all. In excellent shape.

Bidding

Large Needlepoint Tapestry Pattern Canvas PIC (Item #46969997)

Current bid	$9.99
Bid increment	$0.50

*You can buy needlepoint canvases, patterns, and books through Internet auctions like eBay (**http://www.ebay.com**)—and these auctions are free. Use the auction site's search feature to search for "needlepoint." Head to page 40 for more advice on buying stuff through these sites.*

Needlepoint References

A GUIDE TO NEEDLEPOINT
http://www.stitching.com/npg/index.html

Several needlepoint design companies have created a Web-based guide to needlepoint that covers all the basics—from selecting canvas to blocking finished work.

NEEDLEPOINT ONE HOUR ONLINE COURSE & GLOSSARY
http://needlepointfun.com/

Learn how to needlepoint through this online course from Crafts Needlepoint Heirlooms.

TEASURED TIPS
http://www.canvasthepoint.com/story/treasuretips.html

The folks at Canvas The Point share their favorite needlepoint tips. You can add your own tips to the database for others to read.

Needlepoint Discussions

CANVAS THE POINT
http://www.canvasthepoint.com/index.html

This needlepoint shopping site offers a free newsletter, chat area, and a very busy bulletin board where needlepointers discuss everything from wool to hand-painting canvases.

T I P

Use Cross-Stitch Software to Chart Needlepoint

Cross-stitch graphing software is perfect for charting needlepoint. And many of these programs are available for downloading on the Internet. Head to the "Free Stuff for Cross-stitchers" chapter, starting on page 77, for information.

AMERICAN NEEDLEPOINT GUILD DISCUSSION LIST
http://www.needlepoint.org/MailingList.htm

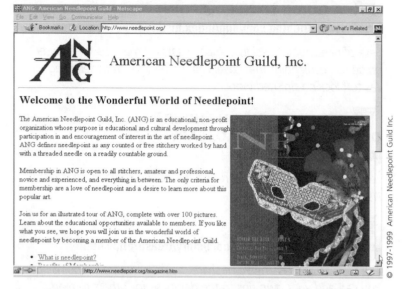

Join a mailing list discussion group of needlepointers by heading to the Web site of the American Needlepoint Guild.

 Needlepoint Guilds

AMERICAN NEEDLEPOINT GUILD
http://www.needlepoint.org/

Tap into the Web site of the ANG for needlepointing advice—and camaraderie.

 Needlepoint Software

BARGELLO DESIGNER
http://www.ayersoft.com/bargello/BD32.html

Ayersoft has designed a Windows 95 program for designing bargello—quilts that is. But you can use it to design needlepoint patterns too. You can download it from their Web site—you only have to pay if you like it.

PRO-STITCH FOR NEEDLEPOINT DESIGN
http://www.rmdinc.net/software.html

Download a demo of Seeker Software's chart design software for PCs and Macs.

FABULOUS FIBERS
http://www.fabulousfibers.com/chenille.htm

© 1999 Pictures & More. Web page created by Right Step Technologies for Pictures & More

O.K., this isn't actually free stuff. But needlepoint wools and other fibers are so hard to find. On Fabulous Fibers' Web site you can click on the yarn type, and the site will display its complete palette. Just click on the yarn to order it.

free Stuff for Plastic Canvas Stitchers

Traditional needlepoint canvas impresses upon one a sense of obligation to stitch nothing but cabbage roses on black. Plastic canvas, in contrast, encourages us to live colorfully. While we stitch dour eyeglasses cases with traditional needlepoint canvas, with plastic canvas we fashion neon pink birdhouses to display on the hutch. From there we proceed to giant rabbits to hang on the door and kitschy purse-clutches that a life-sized Barbie would lug. Is it any surprise that you will find free patterns to stitch all of these things on the Web sites of plastic canvas devotees?

To start your journey, head to **The Plastic Canvas Web Ring** (**http://members.tripod.com/~TheUnii/pcring.html**). A Web ring is a group of enthusiast Web sites that agree to link to each other. You don't need to "join" a Web ring to travel it. All you need to do is click its logo to hop from site to site.

 Plastic Canvas Talk

To join the Plastic Canvas mailing list discussion group run by **Cheryl Perkins** (**victoria@rpmdp.com**) e-mail *majordomo@ml.rpmdp.com.* In the body of the message type just: *subscribe plastic-canvas*. The message will be processed by a computer, not a person. You will get a list of instructions in response.

Another good spot to head for plastic canvas camaraderie is **Janet Perry's Mining Co. Needlepoint** center (**http://needlepoint.miningco.com**).

You'll also find plastic canvassers galore in the **Usenet** newsgroup **alt.crafts.plastic-canvas**, accessible through your browser's news reader or through **Dejanews** (**http://www.dejanews.com**).

Plastic canvas fans also hang out in the mailing list **Knitting** run by Rob McKenzie (*rmckenzi@rpmdp.com*). To subscribe send an e-mail to *majordomo@ml.rpmdp.com* with *subscribe knitting* as the message.

You'll find a big discussion area for plastic canvas at the **Crafty Links Plastic Canvas Bulletin Board (http://www.wwvisions.com/craftbb/plasticcanvas.html)**.

The Biggest Little Craft Mall has set aside a discussion area for plastic canvas devotees at
http://www.craftmall.com/forums/plasticanvas/

You'll find though that a lot of plastic canvas fans tend to hang out with the cross-stitchers (see the "Free Stuff for Cross-Stitchers" chapter, starting on page 77).

Free Pattern Sites

PLASTIC CANVAS ON THE WEB
http://www.vt.edu:10021/V/vsawyer/pc/patframe.html

Vicky Sawyer offers free patterns on her site, as well as instructions on the basics of cutting canvas, beginning and ending threads, and basic stitches.

FREE PLASTIC CANVAS PATTERNS
http://www.angelfire.com/az/freepatterns/index.html

Denise Canez has compiled a whole library of patterns and shares them with cyber-stitchers.

T'S PLASTIC CANVAS DESIGNS
http://www.tsplace.com/index.htm

Teresa Crawford's lovely site offers a stitch guide, project of the month, and lots of links. Projects include an eyeglass case, notebook cover, and "Floppsy the Bunny."

 Plastic Canvas Magazines

PLASTIC CANVAS! MAGAZINE & QUICK & EASY PLASTIC CANVAS
http://www.needlecraftshop.com/

LEWRAN SOFT
http://lewran.com/

You can download free demos of LewRan's Plastic Canvas Software for designing plastic canvas stitching graphs, and PC Converter Picture Software for turning a picture into a plastic canvas stitch chart. Youíll also find at the site free stitch graphs.

 Thinking of Using Blending Filaments with Plastic Canvas?
Visit the Web site of thread-maker Kreinik
(**http://www.kreinik.com**) for a guide to using blending filaments with plastic canvas
(**http://www.kreinik.com/blending.htm#tanget2**).

free Stuff for Beaders

Beads are a universal language. From the African savannahs to glittery high-tech societies, people everywhere have used beads to trade, to admire, to count prayers on, and to embellish themselves and the fabric they wrap around themselves. Anthropologists believe that humans created beads before they invented weaving or other fiber arts. If beads to you mean the plastic kind at Ben Franklin, you're in for a wild trip on the Internet. You'll find beads you never dreamed existed—carved stone animals from Burma, silver beads from Bali, as well as thousands of tutorials for stringing them, sewing them, and even making them. If you like to stitch beads to quilts or clothing, your projects will glow at the creative possibilities that these beading Web sites will bring to you.

Big Web Sites for Beaders

BEADNET
http://www.mcs.net/~simone/beadnet.html

The very first place you should go is Simone Oettinger's BeadNet. Simone, an avid bead embroiderer and weaver, offers an exhaustive directory of beadmaking resources on the Web that includes Web sites of bead artists, bead lore, bead discussion groups, bead sellers, bead museums, and (yes, our favorite) Web sites devoted to bead embroidery.

EMILY HACKBARTH'S THE BEADWORKER
http://exo.com/~emily/beadworker.html

EMILY HACKBARTH'S BEADWORK AT THE MINING CO.
http://beadwork.miningco.com/

Two other terrific sites to get you started are Emily Hackbarth's personal beading page, The Beadworker, and her "guided" site at The Mining Co. The first offers free projects for beginner to intermediate beaders, plus links to shops, tutorials, and other beaders on the Web. At the Mining Co. Emily offers feature articles on beading, plus lessons, discussion, and more links.

TIP

TWE/BEADS
http://www.twebeads.com
For years, Penny Taylor-Wallace has provided zillions of
beads to Fairfield Fashion show garment makers. Visit
her commerical site to see why she's such a favorite.

 Beading Patterns

MARY J. TAFOYA'S "AUNT MOLLY'S BEAD STREET"
http://www.flash.net/~mjtafoya/home.htm

BEADJUNKIES
http://members.tripod.com/~BeadJunkie/

SUZANNE COOPER'S FREE BEAD PATTERNS
http://www.suzannecooper.com/beadwork/beadfreepattern.html

THE BEADER'S CORNER
http://www.fungus.com/arena's/beads.html

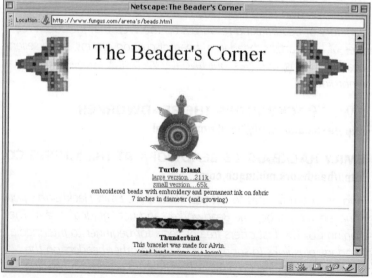

©1999 Arena Reed

MARY J. WINTERS-MEYER'S "THE BEADING BANSHEE"
http://www.staff.uiuc.edu/~mjwmeyer/freedesigns.html

🛒 ANN AND ALAN BRODRICK'S AB ARTGLASS AND BEADWORK PATTERNS
http://www.joust.com/AB/Free_Patterns_Page.html

🛒 RINGS & THINGS' JEWELRY PROJECTS PAGE
http://www.rings-things.com/PROJ1.HTM

🛒 MARGO'S BEADIE CRITTER COLLECTION
http://www.spiritone.com/~pmead/beadwelcome.htm

SONJA'S BEAD GALORE GALLERY
http://www.angelfire.com/mi/beadsgalore/

🔗 *Beading How-Tos*

NATASHA BEADS
http://www.webhaven.com/crick/natasha1/index.htm

Diana Crick shares illustrated instructions for making Nastasha Beads mirror image designs on all four sides of the bead.

MISH'S BEAD-O-RAMA
http://www.accessone.com/~mishwick/beadpage.htm

Although Michele Wickham is no longer an active beader, she leaves up her Web page of beading instructions and diagrams for others to enjoy.

SUZANNE COOPER'S BEADWORK PAGE
http://www.suzannecooper.com/beadmain.html

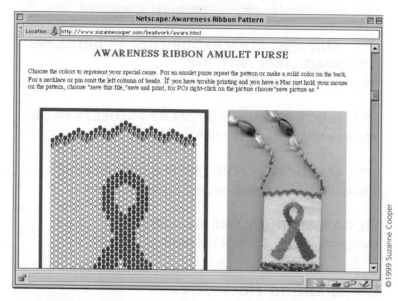

© 1999 Suzanne Cooper

Follow Suzanne's free classroom series to learn beading techniques. Upon completion of the "course" you can print a diploma. You'll also find free patterns and many other things on this information-packed site. Suzanne hosts a beading chat room on the site too.

FOCUSED ON BEADS
http://www.halcyon.com/tarold/techniqs.htm

Cheryl Wolfram teaches you how to make the daisy chain stitch, looming, peyote stitch, and square stitch, plus tells you about the different bead types, their findings and use.

Tap into the Beaders' Web Ring

Find your way to the personal Web pages of beading enthusiasts by heading to **The BeadThing Ring Web Ring** (**http://www.ptw.com/~weezie/beadthg.html**). You don't have to join the ring in order to surf the pages. Click the "Next Page" notation in the Web ring logo.

🛒 BEADWRANGLER'S BEAD AND FIBER JUNCTION
http://www.beadwrangler.com/

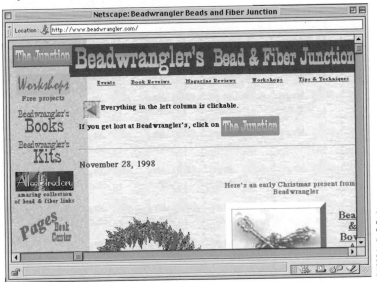

© 1999 Lydia F. Borin

Lydia F. Borin runs this fun site, full of great links and good reads. Be sure to read the "Diary of a Beadaholic" and the "Beadwrangler" stories. Check out the Beadwrangler's tips and techniques.

NATIVE AMERICAN BEADWORK, SEED BEADING TECHNIQUES
http://indy4.fdl.cc.mn.us/~isk/art/beads/art_bea2.html

Paula Giese offers instructions for and illustrations of double-needle appliqué, Peyote beadwork, Lazy Squaw Stitch, and many other America Indian beading techniques.

NATIVE: NATIVE AMERICAN BEADWORK
http://www.nativeweb.org/NativeTech/beadwork/index.html

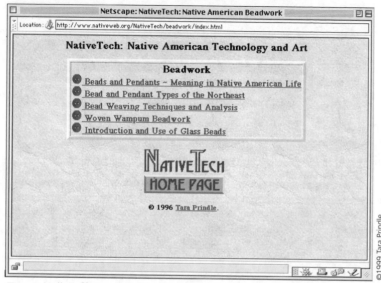

©1999 Tara Prindle

Tara Prindle offers a wealth of information on Indian beading, including bead weaving techniques.

🛒 "STRINGING CORD HINTS AND TIPS" FROM RINGS & THINGS
http://www.rings-things.com/CORD-DET.HTM

ZULU BEADWORK
http://www.marques.co.za/clients/zulu/

Stan and Hilgard Schoeman present gorgeous examples of and illuminating discussions on Zulu beadwork.

"BEAD BASICS" BY PETER FRANCIS, JR.
http://www.thebeadsite.com/BB-DEX.html

Francis serves up an electronic book of bead how-tos, bead discussions, bead illuminations, and even bead reminiscences in his mini electronic book "Beads and Where They Have Led Me."

Beading Resources

Usenet Newsgroup FAQs

Members of the Usenet newsgroups in which beading is discussed regularly assemble and update Frequently Asked Question Files containing beading information that is shared in the newsgroups. These FAQs are:

rec.crafts.jewelry FAQ
rec.crafts.beads Glass Beadmaking FAQ
rec.crafts.beads Beadshops FAQ
rec.crafts.beads Bead Catalogs FAQ
rec.crafts.beads Bead Books FAQ

You'll find them in a variety of places on the Web. (In fact, you can go to any one of the major searchers like **Excite** at **http://www.excite.com**, type in the name of the FAQ, hit the Search button and the searcher will tell you where to go.) An easier way to find them is to head to the Web site of **Colorburst Studios** where you'll find links to all of them (**http://www.teleport.com/~paulec /resources.html**).

 **Buy Czech Beads on the Web**

Czechoslovakia was famous for its beads early in this century. In fact many a flapper wore beads from Czech glass factories. But communists closed the factories. Today you can buy the preserved pre-World War II inventory from many of those factories on the Web. (Isn't this a marvelous age in which we live!) In fact, Web auction sites are great spots to hunt for beautiful antique Czech beads—and many other hard-to-find beads as well. See our tips on pages 40–41 on bargain-hunting on these sites. The best place to look is eBay (**http://www.ebay.com**). Search for "Czech." **Boxlot Online Auction** (**http://www.boxlot.com/**) is another good bead bargain hunter's spot.

More Free Beading Patterns Than You Ever Saw Before!

Carolyn S. Nehring and Eclectic Etc. Beads & Supplies offers a wide variety of beading patterns and tutorials

©1996-1999 Carolyn S. Nehring. All rights reserved

(many lovingly illustrated) in their bi-monthly "Web-zine." You'll find lots of beading projects for kids too (**http://www.ee beads.com /Webzine/**).

BEAD RESOURCES ON-LINE
http://www.mcs.net/~simone/bres.html

Simone Oettinger and BeadNet offer an extensive directory of shops (many on the Net) where you can buy beads, plus catalogs, books, videos, and tools.

🛒 BEADING INFORMATION FOR PROFESSIONAL CRAFTSPEOPLE
http://www.rings-things.com/BEADS.HTM

Another informative site from Rings & Things. Bead definitions, measurements, and conversions

"ETHICS IN BEADWORK" BY SANDI GRAVES
http://www.interweave.com/iwpsite/beadwork/ethics.html

If you see a great beaded purse at a craft show is it ethical to whip out a pad and paper and copy it? If you get a nifty pattern in a class is it moral to photocopy it to pass out to your friends? Find out at this informative site.

ABIGAIL'S BEAD AND TASSEL PAGE
http://beadntassel.hypermart.net/jewelry.html

A contest list, a directory of retreats, exhibitions, and shows are among the offerings on this great site.

 Beading Societies

THE BEAD SOCIETY LIST
http://www.beadwrangler.com/beadsocietylist.htm

From Beadwranglers, a listing of bead societies around the country.

SOCIETY OF BEAD RESEARCHERS
http://www.spiretech.com/~lester/sbr/index/index.htm

SOCIETY OF GLASS BEADMAKERS
http://www.sgb.org/

THE GREAT LAKES BEADWORKERS GUILD
http://www.elbbs.com/glbeadwg/INDEX.HTML

THE BALTIMORE BEAD SOCIETY
http://www.craftwolf.com/baltbd01.htm

THE FAR ISLES MEDIEVAL SOCIETY GUILD OF BEADWORKERS
http://www.weylea.demon.co.uk/farisles/beadwork/index.htm

 Beading Museums and "Virtual" Galleries

THE BEAD MUSEUM
http://www.ariz.com/beads/

Sue Jackson of Northfield, Illinois designed this web site for the museum in Arizon.

NATIVE AMERICAN BEADWORK
http://indy4.fdl.cc.mn.us/~isk/art/beads/beadmenu.html

Paula Giese presents a gallery of Manidoominens or "seed bead" art in Anishnaabemowin, and other Indian beadwork. This is a beautiful and illuminating site!

MOSCOW BEADERS
http://www.ropnet.ru/pages/nidus/gallery/gallery.htm

You'll see some amazing things in this cyber-gallery of beadwork by Russian artists. Items range from jewelry to purses to beaded baskets. Some of the artists offer free patterns.

THE BEAD SITE
http://www.thebeadsite.com/

Peter Francis, Jr. has loaded his site with galleries—as well as chat areas for beaders to congregate.

 ## Beading Magazines

BEAD AND BUTTON
http://www2.beadandbutton.com/beadbutton/

INTERWEAVE BEADWORK
http://www.interweave.com/iwpsite/beadwork/beadwork.html

JEWELRY CRAFTS MAGAZINE
http://www.JewelryCrafts.com/

 ## Beading Discussions
Usenet Newsgroups for Beaders

You'll find lots of other beading enthusiasts in these Usenet newsgroups:
alt.beadworld
rec.crafts.beads
rec.crafts.jewelry
rec.crafts.glass
You can tap in with your browser's newsreader (see Chapter 1 for directions) or by heading to Dejanews
(**http://www.dejanews.com**).

Mailing Lists for Beaders

BEADMAKER
http://www.craftwolf.com/lists

Send an e-mail to list-request@craftwolf.com *with* join beadmaker *or* join beadmaker-digest *in the body of the message.*

BEAD-LIST
http://www.craftwolf.com/lists

Send an e-mail to list-request@craftwolf.com *with* join Bead-List *or* join Bead-List-digest *in the body of the message.*

BEADWORK

Send an e-mail to majordomo@ml.rpmdp.com *with* subscribe bead-work *or* subscribe beadwork-digest *in the body of the message.*

 # Other Mail Lists and Web Discussions

BEADING MAILING LISTS ON ONELIST
http://www.onelist.com

You'll find about a half-dozen beading lists run through OneList. Specialty lists include one for African American Beaders. You can read the messages on OneList's Web site or specify that they be sent to your e-mail box. Head to OneList's Web page and search for "beads" to find the lists.

BEADWORK BULLETIN BOARD AT THE MINING CO.
http://beadwork.miningco.com/

You'll find a bulletin board for discussing beading with others on Emily Hackbarth's beading site at The Mining Co.

BEADING MAILING LISTS ON EGROUPS
http://www.egroups.com

Several mailing lists for beaders are run through the eGroups Web site. To find them head to the main Web page, select the Arts category, head to Crafts, then scroll down the list. You need to join the mailing list (if it is public, some are private), and messages will either be sent to your e-mail box or you can read them on eGroup's Web site.

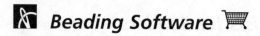 Beading Software

THE BEADER
http://home.att.net./~edhand/Beader/Beader.html

You can download a demo version of the beading pattern design program The Beader. It runs under Windows 95 or NT.

BEADPLAN SOFTWARE FOR BEAD ARTISTS
http://www.BeadPlan.com/

Carlos Portela and Anita Coleman designed this Windows 95 software to draw loom, brick, peyote, and two-drop peyote graphs. You color beads by mouse clicking. No demo is available.

THE BEAD PATTERN DESIGNER
http://beadville.com

Practical Applied Logic, Inc. offers bead design software for Windows 3.x or later. No downloadable demo is available.

BEADSCAPE
http://www.gigagraphica.com/beadscape

Read about this bead design software for Mac users to chart patterns in a variety of weaves like peyote, loom, squared, brick, two-drop, and two-drop one. No downloadable demo is available.

free Stuff for Crocheters

For many of us, our memories of learning to crochet are like the memory of a life-changing experience. Maybe you saw a hippie with a crocheted flower headdress and before you knew it daisies were spilling from your awkwardly wielded crochet hook as your thumb traveled an instruction page. Maybe, as a child, you watched a mysterious, but eccentric neighbor brandishing a hook and as it flew between her fingers the most marvelous lace unfurled over her lap and you knew that you wanted to do that someday. Or perhaps you had a Barbie who's appearance you *just knew* would be improved if she were wearing one of those crocheted Southern belle gowns rather than that idiotic swim suit. The Web is full of goodies for crocheters, from patterns for potholders to ones for sublimely antique lace. You'll also find lots of stitchers involved in crochet-oriented charity projects. Tap in and your life as a crocheter will never be the same.

Crochet Patterns

DOLL CROCHET PARLOR AND POST OFFICE
http://dollcrochet.rpmdp.com/

You'll find free patterns for crocheted dolls, teddies, angels, plus clothes and accessories (such as parasols and party dresses).

SANDI'S CROCHET CABANA
http://www.stcharlesparish.com/crochetcabana/

Sandi offers free patterns plus links to crochet charity sites.

CROCHET PARTNERS PATTERN LIBRARY
http://www.crocheting.com/

CrochetPartners is a big Internet crochet discussion group (see page 121 for directions on signing up). They offer a large pattern library which many Internet crocheters contribute to.

BECKY'S TOUCH OF CROCHET
http://home.earthlink.net/~markzec/bekcraft.html

© 1999 Mark and Becky Zec

Although she was diagnosed with polio at an early age Becky Zec taught herself to crochet. She shares her patterns and offers links to crochet charity projects and her favorite crochet Web sites.

 BEADWRANGLER'S BEAD CROCHET WORKSHOPS
http://www.beadwrangler.com/workshop.htm#Crochet

We know you still yearn to crochet that hippie headdress. You can learn how to combine crocheting with beads at the Beadwrangler. Some of its inspiring projects include the "Marrakech Melody Bag" and "Lydia's Leaves" necklace.

 BY THE HOOK
http://www.angelfire.com/biz/bythehook/index.html

You'll find numerous crochet patterns here. Be sure to ask for a free copy of the newsletter.

THE HAPPY HOOKER ARCHIVES
http://members.aol.com/DREAM13150/PatternIndex.html

Patterns for the "Ozark Hillbilly Potholder," chair caddies and casserole dish covers can be yours at this generous site.

BUZZIN' WITH BEA'S CROCHET
http://hometown.aol.com/crobeanie/homepageindex.html

Bea, aka "Crobeanie" on America Online, shares directions for afghans. Bea also offers links to other goodies for crocheters.

LION BRAND YARNS
http://www.lionbrand.com/

The yarn maker offers free knitting and crochet patterns.

KNITTED THREADS
http://home.earthlink.net/~kthreads/free.htm

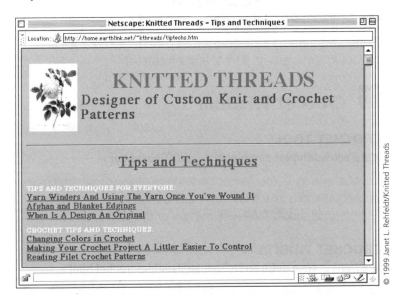

Janet Rehfeldt offers numerous free crochet patterns.

CROCHET IS JUST PLAIN FUN
http://www.somtel.com/~jbolduc/

Julie offers free patterns, an Internet crochet pattern newsletter (for a modest fee), and a chat room for crocheters.

FRIDGIE HIDERS PATTERN INDEX
http://members.aol.com/hewyhooker/patternindex.html

Festoon your fridge with angels, bees, and Amish folk with the free patterns on this resplendent site.

SUNSITE CROCHET PATTERN ARCHIVE
http://sunsite.doc.ic.ac.uk/recreation/crafts/fido-cfdn/cfk-pat/

Sunsite is a large software and file directory in the United Kingdom, home to the venerable FidoNet BBS network, and that's where some of these patterns originated.

PROJECTS FROM SOLUTIA, INC.
http://www.thesmartyarns.com/project1.html

Solutia Inc., formerly Monsanto, offers patterns for floral pillows, lots of afghans, vests, pullovers, and a waistcoat.

 ## Crochet Wisdom

CROCHET TOOLS
http://www.teleport.com/~noelvn/cp/CPTools.html

Lee Mathewson & Noel Nevins have compiled answers to common crochet questions like, "How do I make a blocking board?" and "Which hook should I use with this size of thread?"

CROCHET TIDBITS
http://www.scsn.net/users/ckeenan/dsunkle/crochet.html

Dawn offers guides to metric conversions, yarn and needle conversions, a guide to abbreviations, plus crochet tips.

ASK NITA
http://members.aol.com/nitalittle/home.htm

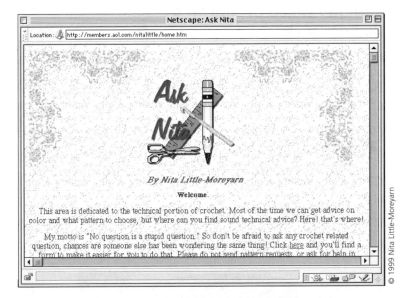

© 1999 Nita Little-Moreyarn

Ask Nita Little-Moreyarn your crochet questions or search her archives for answers to other crocheters' questions.

J. BARRETT'S KNIT TO CROCHET CONVERSIONS
http://www.scsn.net/users/ckeenan/dsunkle/cro-knit.html

J. Barrett explains how to turn a knitting pattern into a crochet one.

CROCHET MUSINGS' LEARN TO CROCHET TUTORIAL
http://crochet.rpmdp.com/tutorial.html

Deb Arrowood explains the basics of crochet, comments on stitches from picot to popcorn, plus discusses the choice of hooks and yarn.

Crochet Guilds

CROCHET GUILD OF AMERICA
http://www.crochet.org/

If you crochet you really should join the CGA for fun, camaraderie and inspiration. You'll find on its Web site not only membership information, but also thorough crochet lessons (even for lefties). The CGA also conducts numerous charity projects.

Crochet Discussion Groups

CROCHET MUSINGS WEB SITE HOME PAGE
http://crochet.rpmdp.com/

©1999 Deb Arrowood

*Sign up for Deb Arrowood's **Crochet List**, an e-mail discussion group, at this site. You can also participate in live chats through their **#Crochet chat channel*** (**http://crochet.rpmdp.com /chat.html**).

CROCHET PARTNERS E-MAIL LIST
http://www.bizfocus.com/CP/subreq.htm

CrochetPartners is a huge and active e-mail mailing list discussion group run by Rae French. You can sign up at its Web site or e-mail majordomo@bizfocus.com *OR* majordomo@lists.dynamicweb.net *with* subscribe crochetpartners <YourRealName> <Your e-mail Address> *as in* subscribe crochetpartners Laura Smith lsmith@aol.com *in the body of the message.*

CAFE CROCHET
http://bizfocus.com/CP/CafeCrochet/

This marvelous Web site is run by CrochetPartners. It offers message boards, a live chat link, and links to the Usenet textile and craft newsgroups. It also offers CrochetPartners own newsgroup.

CROCHET DOLL PARLOR MAILING LIST
http://dollcrochet.rpmdp.com/info.html

To join this group devoted to discussing crocheted dolls and clothes send an e-mail to majordomo@ml.rpmdp.com. *In the body of the message type:* subscribe dollcrochet. *Do not type anything else in the e-mail message. (If you have a signature file in your mail program you will need to disable it before sending this message because it will confuse the receiving computer.)*

KNITTING

*Don't let the name deter you. This list, run by Rob McKenzie (*rmckenzi@rpmdp.com*), is also for discussing crochet. To subscribe send an e-mail to* majordomo@ml.rpmdp.com *with* subscribe knitting *as the message.*

Searching for Vintage Crochet Patterns?

See pages 86–87 for advice on how to track down vintage needlework patterns on the Web—or bid on them through Web auctions!

CROCHET AT THE MINING COMPANY
http://crochet.tqn.com/

Sandi Marshall hosts this terrific site for crocheters, which offers a bulletin board and chat room, plus loads of links to other crochet resources on the Net.

 THE BIGGEST LITTLE CRAFT MALL CROCHET FORUM
http://www.craftmall.com/forums/

You'll find a crochet discussion group at this commercial site.

Looking for Crochet Magazines?

You can type the words "crochet magazine" into a searcher like **Excite** (**http://www.excite.com**) and the searcher will come up with magazine services that sell various titles like **Crochet Fantasy** at a discount. You can also head to Barnes & Noble's (**http://www.barnesandnoble.com**) for what we think is the biggest, nicest magazine subscription database on the Web. Plus, you can have confidence ordering from **Barnes & Noble**; they're not some fly-by-night operation you stumble on through a searcher. Another very good magazine service is the **Reception Room Service** (**http://www.rrs.com**). They sell thousands of titles—many craft magazines, and at least a dozen crochet ones—at deep discounts. (To easily search one of their jammed pages, in your browser, select Edit/Find in Page, then type "crochet.")

CHAPTER 10

free Stuff for Tatters and Other Lacemakers

For years you thought that you and that nun in Colorado who won the National Endowment for the Arts grant for bobbin lace-making were the only souls in the cosmos who knotted thread into delicate butterflies. But one day you tapped into the Web and it seemed everywhere you looked you found Web pages for tatters, plus tutorials on long-forgotten forms of lace-making you had never heard of before. The Web has grown into a rich library of information on lacemaking, both its practice and history, as well as an ever-growing repository of patterns. You'll find lots of fun and quirky things too: such as directions on how to make lacemaking bobbins out of cattle bones and a pattern for a tatted motorcycle. Next thing you know someone will invent a mouse that can double as a shuttle.

Tatting

THE ELEGANT ART OF TATTING
http://www.elysian.com.au/tatting/

You'll find lots of patterns on this lovely site, plus tips.

CARRIE'S TATTING INSTRUCTION PAGE
http://www.mich.com/~carlson/tat/tat.html

Carrie Carlson shares exceptional, well-illustrated lessons.

TERRY THE TATTER'S HOME PAGE
http://www.best.com/~jimm/ttt/

Terry offers free instructions for ornaments on this enjoyable page.

THIS 'N' TAT
http://www.capital.net/~ltrumble/index.html

Lisa Trumble helps us tat better with free lessons and patterns.

STEPH'S STRING RELATEDSTUFF
http://www.sandbenders.demon.co.uk/

Stephanie Peters of Manchester, England offers information on various forms of lacemaking including tatting and bobbin lacemaking.

NANCY'S TATTING PAGE
http://www.frii.com/~nprice/tat.htm

Nancy Price shares her tatting patterns and links.

All material©1992-1999 Lisa C. Trumble. All rights reserved

TATTING AND THE SHUTTLESMITH
http://www.radiks.net/~guzzi/shuttle.html

Netscape: Tatting and The ShuttleSmith

Location: http://www.radiks.net/~guzzi/shuttle.html

Karen's Tatting Page and *The ShuttleSmith*

Here's my attempt to link my two passions together--motorcycling and tatting. For the past 5 years or so I have been studying advanced tatting techniques. It seemed to me that the best way to test my understanding of the various techniques was to design a tatted piece incorporating them. Motorcycling was my inspiration.

I started by finding a nice simple picture of a motorcycle. My husband and I ride European motorcycles so there was a large array of styles to choose from for inspiration. I decided on a 60's model Triumph and then set out to get as much detail as possible to have it identifiable as such a model.

Every stitch on my motorcycle is TATTED!

© 1997-1999 Karen Bovard

Karen Bovard explains her need to marry her two passions—motorcycling and tatting—and so shares with cyberspace her pattern for a tatted "hog."

NORTHTIPTON'S NEEDLE TATTING
http://www.3wave.com/northtipton/tatting.htm

Needle tatting is tatting with needles rather than a shuttle. Cathie Sanders offers tutorials, free patterns—plus encouragements to knitters to use needle-tatting to do things like join afghan panels.

NEEDLE TATTING FROM HANDPRINT PRESS
http://ourworld.compuserve.com/homepages/HandPrint_Press/
needleta.htm

Leisa ReFalo's page includes some history, comparisons between needle tatting and shuttle tatting, clear stitch diagrams, and patterns. There's also a link to explanations of French, German, Italian, and Spanish tatting terms.

Bobbin and Other Lacemaking

ARACHNE'S WEB: THE LACEMAKER'S HOME PAGE
http://www.arachne.com/

Liz Reynolds' Arachne's Web Server focuses on 16th and early 17th century laces. She offers links to guilds and suppliers.

HEIDI'S BOBBIN LACE
http://www.clark.net/pub/heidi/lace/

Heidi offers a collection of links to lacemaking resources on the Web, plus her bobbin lace class notes.

BEAUTIFUL NETTING
http://www.the-spa.com/bartholomew/netting/

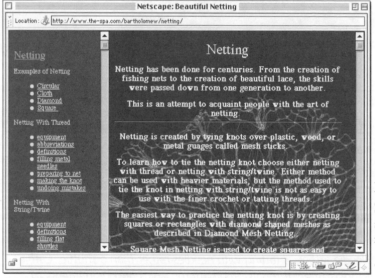

Created by Rita F. Bartholomew

Netting is the art of lacemaking by tying knots over gauges. Rita Bartholomew has created what is perhaps the consumate cyber-space source of information on this ancient art (as old as fishermen and their nets). She also offers patterns.

When Web Sites Are as Delicate as Lace

For some reason tatting and other lace-making Web sites tend to be ephemeral. They're there one day, gone the next. That's because these sites are put up by enthusiasts and are less apt to have commercial elements than other craft sites. If you can't find the lace-making sites you'd like to visit, check out some of the discussion groups listed in the following pages for recommendations of sites.

BOBBIN LACE
http://www.net-wave.or.jp/~won-c/bobin/bobine.html

Wonder Creator, Inc. shares an assortment of pictures, many with English explanations, of bobbin lace from Japan.

POOLE BOBBIN LACE CIRCLE
http://users.bournemouth-net.co.uk/~pblc.cyberlink

You'll find here free patterns, a nice assortment of lace-related Web links, and friendly fellow lace-makers.

TURNING LACE BOBBINS
http://users.mwci.net/~rspragg/lacebob.html

Robert Spragg Sr. explains how to use cattle and horse bones to create the delicate bobbins necessary for lacemaking (bone bobbins are where the term "bone lace" originated). The less ambitious can use nails or clothespins.

JEAN WEATHERFORD'S LACEMAKING
http://home.rmi.net/~mweather/lacemkg.html

Jean Weatherford shares a pattern for a spectacular bobbin lace cross (it will put your tatted Bible bookmarks to shame), plus links to lacemaking suppliers on the Web.

LACIS
http://www.lacis.com

This Berkeley, California lacemaking supplies seller offers a wonderful collection of links to lace information around the Web.

Lacemaking History

LEGACY OF LACE
http://www.legacyoflace.com/

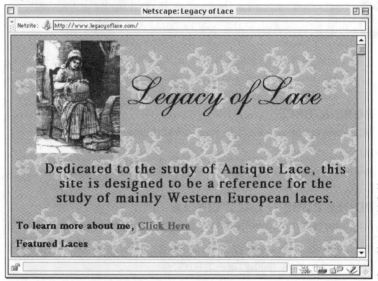

Created by Joeanna M. Smith

If you think 18th century Valenciennes with round ground is a kind of fancy hamburger, you need to brush up on your lace history. Joeanna Smith's extensive Web site will introduce you to all the different breeds of vintage lace. You'll read some fascinating stories on the site, like how a Belgian women's campaign in WWI helped rejuvenate the Belgian lace industry, despite the Germans' efforts to quash it.

BELGIUM BRUSSELS: THE HISTORY OF LACE
http://209.41.63.136/belgium-lace-history.htm

Learn about the history of Belgian lacemaking, courtesy of the Belgium Travel Network.

REAL BELGIAN LACE MANUFACTORY
http://www.belgian-lace.com/index.htm

This Web site in Brussels, Belgium features a gallery and history of Belgian lace.

 Lace Magazines

LACE MAGAZINE
http://www.lacemagazine.com/

Visit the home of Lace Magazine, and learn about lace history and techniques.

LACE MAGAZINE FROM THE BRITISH LACE GUILD
http://www.laceguild.demon.co.uk/LG/LM/lm.html

The British Lace Guild publishes a wonderful quarterly magazine for members, and some of its features, including free patterns, are available on its Web site. (We love the one for the lace Christmas "cake band"—an elaborate swatch of lace that is wrapped around a cake. [http://www.laceguild.demon.co.uk/LG/LM/Pattern0498.html] It looks like something one would see on their grandma's buffet. The cake looks pretty yummy too.)

Lace Museums

THE ALLHALLOWS MUSEUM IN DEVON, ENGLAND
http://www.cyberlink.co.uk/allhallows

Give us a plane ticket to Devon! This quaint musuem, nestled in a 14th century chapel, houses an exhibit of prehistoric artifacts that hail back to the Stone, Bronze, and Iron Ages as well as a world-famous gallery of lace. You can buy bobbins and postcards from the museum at the site.

BOBBIN LACE EUROPEAN NETWORK
http://www.blen.net/

When we visited this site it was under construction, and home to future "virtual lace museums" of museum collections in Portugal, Czechoslavakia, and Finland. Hopefully by the time you read this those galleries will have opened.

THE LACE MUSEUM & GUILD
http://www.thelacemuseum.org/index.html

The Lace Museum was founded by a group of women in the San Francisco Bay area. They offer a free pattern and newsletter on their Web site.

𝕜 *Lacemaking Guilds*

INTERNATIONAL OLD LACERS
http://members.aol.com/IOLinc/ioli.html

Find out about this group for anyone who loves lace, including those who make it and those who collect it. The site also offers a great selection of lacemaking links to information on the Web.

INTERNATIONAL BOBBIN AND NEEDLE LACE ORGANIZATION
http://www.bitbetter.com/oidfa/

This group of lace-makers is based in France, but members from around the world are welcome.

THE BRITISH LACE GUILD
http://www.laceguild.demon.co.uk/

This is a great site! You can read about the art of lacemaking, find lists of suppliers, and read excerpts from this British Guild's wonderful magazine Lace Magazine.

ARACHNE'S WEB GUIDE TO CANADIAN LACEMAKING GUILDS
http://www.arachne.com/guild/canada.html

Arachne's Web offers a list of the street addresses of Canadian lace-making clubs.

 Lacemaking Discussions

ARACHNE'S LACEMAKERS' MAILING LIST
http://www.arachne.com/list_instructions.html

Arachne's is the leading lacemakers' discussion group on the Web, with over 500 members. Tap into this Web page to find out how to join. Before you join though, be sure to read the members' handbook at **ftp://ftp.arachne.com/lace-archive/Handbook.txt**. There are two versions of the list—Lace-List and Lace-Chat. The former is strictly lace-related messages, while the latter includes conversational chit-chat. You can also read archives of past messages in both lists at **ftp://ftp.arachne.com/lace-archive/**.

THE BIGGEST LITTLE CRAFT MALL TATTING FORUM
http://www.craftmall.com/forums/tatting/

The Biggest Little Craft Mall, a commercial Web site, offers a tatting bulletin board, but discussion was sparse when we visited. Maybe the conversation will pick up.

LACE

To subscribe e-mail majordomo@panix.com with subscribe lace <Your real name> <Your e-mail address> as the message, as in subscribe lace Jan Lacey janlacey@crafters.com

THE TATTING MAILING LIST
http://www.elysian.com.au/tatting/

This lively discussion group, devoted exclusively to tatting, was formed from an overflow of members in Arachne.

TATCHAT PAGE
http://www.fortunecity.com/victorian/vangogh/235/

This is the home page for the TatChat mailing list. You'll find information on how to subscribe, plus archives of previous lists, patterns, tutorials, and more.

TEXTILE.ORG'S LACEMAKING BULLETIN BOARD
http://www.textiles.org/cgi-bin/view_bb2?Category=Lacemaking

Textile.Org is a large site devoted to the textile arts (**http://www.textiles.org**). *Although when we visited no lacemakers were present, you can start your own lacemaking discussion here.*

Lacemaking Software

STEPHANIE PETERS' GRID GENERATOR PROGRAM
http://www.sandbenders.demon.co.uk/dots.htm

Stephanie Peters of Manchester, England has created a program for Windows 95/98 and NT 4 which generates grids of dots for lacemaking. It also runs on a Mac running SoftWindows or VirtualPC. The grids can be used with other software. The software is free, but only for personal, non-professional use.

IL-SOFT LACE DESIGNER
http://www.ilsoft.co.uk/

You can download here free demonstration versions of Lace Designer Gold and Lace Designer Gold Lite. You can use the software to design charts for numerous kinds of lacemaking including Torchon, Bucks, Beds, and Honiton. They run on Windows-running PCs.

Travel the Lacemaker's Web Ring

A "Web ring" is a group of Web sites that agree to link to each other via a special logo. You click on the logo and you are speeded to member sites in the ring. There is a **Lace and Lacemaking Web Ring** that will take you to the Web sites of lacemakers around the world. To tap in, or to find out how to join, head to **Ana's** page at **http://www.netcentral.co.uk/~geoffana//lacering/index.html**

The Lace and Lacemaking
WebRing

[Prev | Next 5 | Random | Next]
[Lace & Lacemaking WebRing Index]
Want to add your Lace site?

The Usenet Crafts/Textile FAQs

http://www.cs.uu.nl/wais/html/na-dir/crafts/textiles/faq/.html
Read answers to fiber-related questions relating to knitting, weaving, spinning, and other fiber crafts as posted in the Usenet newsgroups.

Frequently Asked Questions About the Stringy Stuff Hanging from Needles and Hooks

http://www.woolworks.org/fibers.html
Emily Way tells you about the different fibers used to knit and crochet.

free Stuff for Rug Makers

We're all familiar with the rug hooking kits with the packets of acrylic yarn that you buy at craft stores. But there are many other kinds of rug making. There's rug braiding—the method used by our grandmothers when they braided old rags into kitchen rugs to be economical. There's rug weaving on a loom. There are appliqué rag rugs. There are patched, tambour, Amish knotted, and crocheted rugs. And there's "traditional rug hooking." Traditional rug hooking is the method American colonists used to loop fabric or yarn through a canvas-like backing—usually feedsack—to create heavy rugs that were often bright with patterns or folk art-style pictures. Most of the rug makers you'll meet on the Web are "traditional rug hookers." But many other kinds of rug makers like latch hookers and weavers congregate in cyberspace too.

General Rug Making Web Sites

Here are some Web sites where you'll find general information on rug making, including links to Web resources for specific kinds of rug creation.

Design Your Own Braided Rug with Braid Wizard

You can download a free demo of Luis Michal's $40 shareware program **Braid Wizard** (**http://www.buscapique.com/newworld.htm**) for Windows 3.x and later, which will help you design braided rugs. You can choose from different rug shapes and braiding techniques, choose the color scheme and specify the size. You can make the rug yourself, (a $50 version of the program will give you braiding instructions) or simply click a button and Michal will braid the rug for you for a modest fee.

RUG HOOKERS NETWORK
http://www.rughookersnetwork.com/

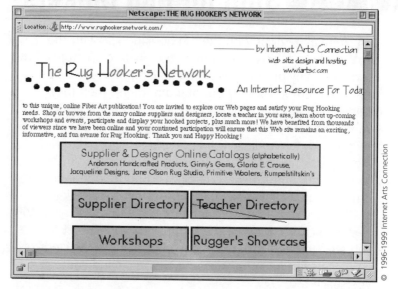

The Rug Hookers Network offers a bulletin board for those who want to discuss different types of rug making, plus a list of suppliers of hard-to-find rug making tools and materials, and links to rug-hooking guilds around the country

THE RUGCREATING E-MAIL LIST
http://www.onelist.com

You can join this restricted e-mail list by heading to OneList (URL above) or e-mailing list owner Shannon at robngsmom@aol.com. This is a private list which means you need permission to join.

Commune with Other Ruggers on Usenet

You'll find other rug makers chatting in various Usenet newsgroups including **uk.rec.crafts** (a newsgroup for United Kingdom crafters), **rec.crafts.textiles.yarn**, **rec.crafts.textiles.misc**, and **rec.crafts.textiles.needlework**. An easy way to find the message strings is to head to **Dejanews** (**http://www.dejanews.com**) and type "rug" in the search form.

RUG MAKERS HOMESTEAD
http://www.netw.com/~rafter4/

© 1999 Diana Blake Gray

*Rafter-Four Designs and Diana Blake Gray offer information on many different kinds of rug making, plus a terrific list of Sources for Rugmakers on the Internet (**http://www.netw.com/~rafter4/net.html**).*

 # *Stuff for "Traditional" Rug Hookers*

HOOKED!
THE TRADITIONAL RUG HOOKING HOME PAGE
http://www.rughookingonline.com/hooked/hooked.html

Deborah Merriam pioneered one of the Internet's first "e-zines" or electronic magazines that are distributed via e-mail. She still publishes it—it's called Woolgatherings *and it's the premier electronic publication—and gathering spot for traditional rug hookers.* Woolgatherings' *Web site, which is sponsored by* Rug Hooking *magazine (see the address on page 138), offers FAQs, extensive links to rug-making resources on the Web, a guide to rug galleries, rug cleaning information, plus archives of past discussions in* Woolgatherings.

AOL RUGGERS
http://members.aol.com/DUST/index.html

AOL RUGGERS NEWSLETTER
http://www.rughookingonline.com/hooked/AOLindex.html

The AOL Ruggers are a group of traditional rug hookers on America Online who congregate via weekly chats and share an e-mail newsletter. Visit their Web site to find out more, and tap into archives of their newsletter courtesy of Deborah Merriam and Rug Hooking *magazine.*

RUG HOOKING ONLINE
http://www.rughookingonline.com/

Rug Hooking *magazine publishes an incredible Web site where you can read a wide range of articles from past issues on topics like reproducing stained glass designs in rugs, different kinds of rug backings, and extensive information on dyeing. You'll find FAQs, tutorials, and links to rug hooking information around the Web. You'll find an archive of free patterns and past articles from the magazine at* **http://www.rughookingonline.com/archives.html**.

PADULA: HOOKED RUGMAKING ONLINE
http://www.rughookingonline.com/hooked/padula.html

Padula is a mailing list discussion group for traditional rug hookers. To subscribe, send an e-mail to majordomo@lists.southwind.net. *In the body of the message type:* subscribe padula.

Stuff for Rug Latch Hookers

PAUL MILLER'S "THE LATCH HOOK PAGE"
http://www.angelfire.com/la/latchhook/

Miller tells how latch hooking became his passion, and shares his tips and techniques, including how he creates his own designs and transfers them from newspaper to canvas with a laundry marker. He shares pictures of his grandchildren and the rugs he's made for them—with custom labels lovingly printed "Made by Grandpa Miller."

 Stuff for Rug Weavers

THE RUG WEAVERS WORKSHOP
http://www.rugweavers.com/

©1999 Pamela Aossey

If you weave rugs this is the site for you. Sign up for Rug Talk, *the rug weavers mailing list. Read features on rug weaving, tips, and view beautiful rugs that other rug weavers on the Web have created.*

RUG WEAVING WORKSHOP MAILING LIST

To subscribe e-mail qpk@patriot.net with RWW in the subject line.

 Miscellaneous Rug Lovers' Resources

 CYBER RUG CENTER GALLERY
http://www.cyberrug.com/american.htm

You'll see some marvelous antique rugs in the gallery of this site.

ORIENTAL RUG REVIEW
http://www.rugreview.com/orr.htm

Read articles from past issues of this journal for fans and collectors of Oriental rugs and other textiles.

"RUG HISTORY AND DEFINITIONS" FROM WOVEN TREASURES
http://www.woventreasures.com/rugs/definitions/definits.htm

Learn the difference between Kashan and Ferahan rugs and the history of different types of rugs.

free Stuff for Spinners

CHAPTER 12

The Internet is probably responsible for more converts to the ancient art of spinning than any book or magazine article. You start as a humble knitter or weaver and through the encouragement of others discover that a wheel or simple spindle can bring a new world of fibers to your fingertips. A Web page can't show you how to hold your fingers to guide the fibers as expertly as another spinner can, but the Web does offer insight, buying advice, and most importantly, the friendship of spinners around the globe. That alone will prove your most valuable resource as a spinner.

 Head to the Free Stuff for Knitters chapter, starting on page 42, as well as the ones for Weavers on page 149 for more spinning-related links.

Spinning How-Tos

🛒 HOW TO USE THE DROP SPINDLE
http://www.handspinning.com/lollipops/spininst.htm

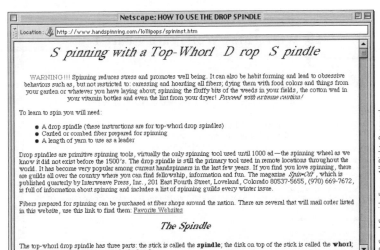

Carol Cassidy-Fayer teaches you how to spin using a top-whorl drop spindle.

🛒 "SELECTING A SPINNING WHEEL" FROM THE WOOLERY
http://ww1.woolery.com/webpages/jive/selectwheel.html

If you know nothing about spinning wheels but are thinking of buying one, this is a good place to start learning. The Woolery offers a guide to the types, the technical terms, and the attachments.

🛒 "SPINDLES" BY KATHRYN OF THE HILLS
http://www.cobweb.net/~ryn/spindles.html

Kathryn Wells offers history, perspectives, and a lesson on how to use a drop spindle.

"MAKING AN ANDEAN PLYING BRACELET" BY SHARON MCCARTER
http://www.mindex.com/users/sharon/andean/index.html

McCarter explains how to make an Andean plying bracelet, for those times when you have a spindle full of singles.

"WOLF TALES/MAKING YARN" BY JERILYN MONROE
http://www.inetdesign.com/wolfdunn/Yarn1.html

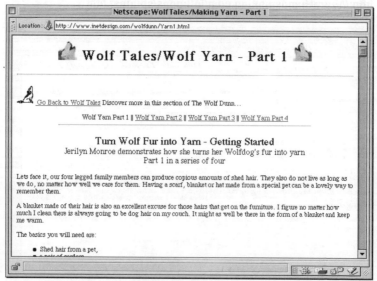

Monroe demonstrates how she turns her wolf dog's fur into yarn.

Spinning Information and photos on this web page by Jeri Monroe. ©1999
©1999 Gudrun F. Dunn and the Wolf Dunn.

"HAND SPINNING DOG HAIR" BY PATTY LEE DRANCHAK
http://www.waterw.com/~pattylee/

© 1999 PAtty Lee Dranchak

Dranchak offers excellent advice on putting dog hair to work.

STEPS IN PROCESSING WOOL INTO YARN
http://www.blackberry-ridge.com/prosdscr.htm

Blackberry Ridge Woolen Mill offers a guided tour to show how wool makes its way into yarn.

Good Spinning Resources

FAQS ABOUT SPINNING WHEELS
http://www.jb.man.ac.uk/~caj/wheel.html

Christine Jordan has compiled an absolutely wonderful resource by culling spinning-related postings in Knit List and the Weavers, Spinners & Dyers mailing list. Learn about the differences between brands of wheels, name of wheel parts, and so much more. She also offers a great assortment of links to other spinning resources on the Web.

THE SPIN LIST ARCHIVES
http://www.spinning.net/archives/index.html

You can read and search past messages exchanged in the large e-mail mailing list Spin. Information spans a wide range of topics.

SPINNING AT THE MINING CO.
http://spinning.miningco.com/

Rosemary Brock hosts this dynamic "cyber-magazine" of features and links about spinning.

DELPHI TEXTILE ARTS FORUM
http://www.delphi.com/textile

Ever since this forum was founded by spinning and fiber guru Susan Druding nearly a decade ago, TAF has been the premier cyber-hang out for spinners. Read an ever-changing collection of feature stories, links, and often outrageous opinions.

🛒 SPIN-OFF
http://www.interweave.com/iwpsite/spin_off/spinoff.html

The Web site of this Interweave magazine offers feature clips and more.

🛒 COLLECTED WISDOM FROM THE ASHFORD-SPINNERS E-MAIL LIST
http://www.straw.com/cpy/wisdom/

Using and preserving wheels, how to appy finish, and teaching kids spinning are some of the many topics addressed in the archives of the Ashford-Spinners e-mail group, offered by Straw Into Gold.

🛒 ASHFORD SPINNING & WEAVING
http://www.ashford.co.nz/

Visit the Web site of spinning wheel maker Ashford, and find answers to your questions about how to clean and maintain your wheel. You can also get a free fiber arts magazine.

STRAW INTO GOLD
http://www.straw.com

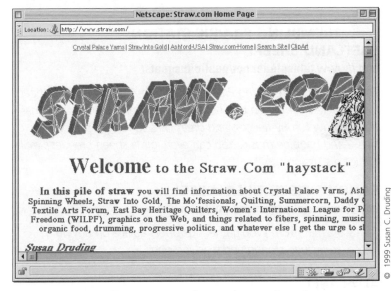

Netscape: Straw.com Home Page

Location: http://www.straw.com/

Crystal Palace Yarns | Straw Into Gold | Ashford-USA | Straw.com-Home | Search Site | ClipArt

STRAW . COM

Welcome to the Straw.Com "haystack"

In this pile of straw you will find information about Crystal Palace Yarns, Ash
Spinning Wheels, Straw Into Gold, The Mo'fessionals, Quilting, Summercorn, Daddy
Textile Arts Forum, East Bay Heritage Quilters, Women's International League for P
Freedom (WILPF), graphics on the Web, and things related to fibers, spinning, music
organic food, drumming, progressive politics, and whatever else I get the urge to s

Susan Druding

© 1999 Susan C. Druding

Straw Into Gold offers many excellent resources for spinners.

🛒 SPINNERS' AND WEAVERS' HOUSECLEANING PAGES
http://together.net/~kbruce/kbbspin.html

Kathleen Bruce runs this free service where non-commercial spinners can resell "gently used" spinning and weaving equipment.

SPINDLITIS!
http://www.xws.com/terispage/spindle.html

Teri Pittman runs a great Web site for spinners who collect drop spindles. You'll also find reviews, information on spinning tools, and links.

⚡ Advice About Sheep (and Their Fleeces)

🛒 TREMBLING PRAIRIE STATION: SHETLAND SHEEP
http://www.telusplanet.net/public/tpsgoats/

The Web site of Trembling Prairie Station, an Alberta, Canada sheep farm, offers information on Shetland sheep, spinning tips, information on how to buy fleeces, and great links to related fiber art sites—and bagpipe music. You can even join a sheep breeder's mailing list discussion.

SANDY'S FIBER TIPS/FLEECE
http://www.webports.com/woolg/tip.htm

Sandy Sitzman from Woolgatherings offers advice on buying a fleece, to include storing and washing one.

ALPACANET
http://www.alpacanet.com/

Don't forget alpacas! Visit Alpacanet to learn about this luxurious fiber, including how to clean and store it.

Visit Web Sites of Spinners' Guilds Around the World

Tap into **Christine Jordan's Web page (http://www.jb .man.ac.uk/~caj/wheel.html)** for an up-to-date list of spinning guild Web sites.

Spinning Discussions

You'll find spinners lurking in cyberspace wherever fiber fans congregate, but one of the best spots to go to find them are the **Usenet** newsgroups **rec.crafts.textiles.yarn** and **rec.crafts.textiles.misc**.

You'll also find spinners in **CompuServe's** Fibercrafts forum (use the go word "fibercrafts" to get there).

On **America Online** head to the Needlecrafts center by using the keyword "needlecraft." You can also get information on AOL spinning chats by heading to the Web site **Puggle's Guide to AOL's Spinning & Weaving Chat Information** (**http://members.aol.com/hostpuggle/chatpg.html**).

 Web Sites Where Spinners Hang-Out

DELPHI TEXTILE ARTS FORUM
http://www.delphi.com/textile

Spinners and other fiber devotees abound on Delphi's bulletin boards. This is also home to the Northwest Regional Spinners Association and the Ashford Joy Spinners.

SPINNING & DYEING AT THE MINING CO.
http://spinning.miningco.com/

 Mailing Lists

SPIN LIST
http://www.spinning.net/

Spin List is a very active e-mail group of spinners ranging from beginners to professionals.

SPINNERS

E-mail spinning-list-request@eskimo.com. Type subscribe in the subject line and the body of the message.

**Travel the Personal Pages of Fiber Fans
With the Fiber Art Ring**

A Web "ring" connects pages of enthusiasts.
You can "travel" the pages of members of the
Fiber Art ring by tapping into a member's site,
like that of **Ron Parker's Fiber Home**
(**http://www.angelfire.com/mn/FiberHome/WebRing.html**).

SPINDLITIS
http://www.xws.com/terispage/spindle.html

Visit Teri Pittman's Web page or e-mail spindle@xws.com. *In the
subject line, type* subscribe *or* subscribe digest.

KNIT-SPIN
http://www.keyway.net/crafts/

*Fran Lesh runs a list for knitters. You can read archives of the list by
heading to this site too.*

SHEEP-L

*It's inevitable: you start spinning and soon you want your own
sheep. Join other spinning sheep raisers in this mailing list by
e-mailing* listserv@listserv.uu.se *with* subscribe sheep-l *in the
message and find out if your backyard is big enough.*

NOTJUSTSHEEP OR "NOTSHEEP"
http://www.craftwolf.com/lists

*Wheat Carr runs this list for talking about all fiber producing ani-
mals and using their fiber in needlework.*

free Stuff for Weavers

No needleart is so much like the human spirit as weaving. Anthropologists attribute its invention to Neolithic man weaving beads and string in ceremonial aprons during his emergence as a farmer, trader, and traveler. In pre-war Germany weavers in the Bauhaus married art and technology to create a revolution in textiles. When Nazis interred many of the weavers in death camps, their students and disciples worked on, and from different quarters of the world nurtured a renaissance in hand-weaving that was as vibrant as their teachers' spirits. Weaving, like the human spirit, is indomitable. You'll meet weavers from every corner of the world in cyberspace. For years the online service Compuserve has been a favorite haunt of weavers. (If you're a member use the "go" word "fibercrafts" to get to them.) One could easily devote a book to all the things for weavers on the Web. We've tried to cull the essentials, but even that was hard.

 ## Big Weaving Web Sites

RON'S FIBER HOME
http://www.angelfire.com/mn/FiberHome/

This site isn't more than a small collection of links, at least for now. Its owner Ron Parker ran perhaps the first and only computer bulletin board for weavers many moons ago in pre-Internet days. There was something magical about logging into Ron's board through crackly phone lines late at night. Screens with slowly scrolling green letters greeted callers. We think that Ron, his FiberNet mailing list, and his weaver pals are at the spiritual center of weaving in cyberspace, so we suggest you visit his Web site first.

WEAVING ON DELPHI
http://www.delphi.com/textile/

Many weavers congregate in the Textile Arts Forum on the Delphi Web site, run by Rita Levine and founded by Susan Druding. You'll also find files, features, and chat here.

Visit Puggles' Guide to Weaver Math

"Using Factor Pairs to Sley the Reed" is one of the headlines on Puggles' weaver math page (**http://members.aol.co/hostpuggle/wevmath.html**). Neither Gloria nor Judy have any idea of what this means. For all we know it could be from Lewis Carroll. "Tis brillig to sley the reed!" Visit **Puggle's Wondrous Weaving Page** (**http://members .aol.com/hostpuggle/weavepg.html**) for more tips, plus directions on how to tap into the weekly AOL weavers' chats.

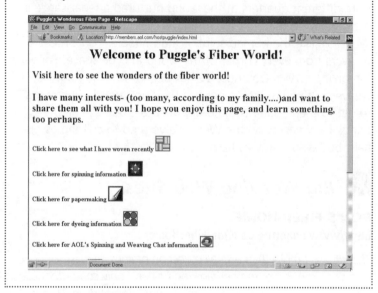

WEAVING FROM THE MINING CO.
http://weaving.miningco.com/

Päivi Suomi is your guide. She provides lots of links to weaving around the Web, plus regular articles, updates, and chats.

THE WEAVER'S HAND
http://w3.thegroup.net/~janis/

Janis Saunders offers an extensive guide to resources on the Web for practitioners of tablet weaving, Kumihimo, and ply-splitting.

 Weaving How-Tos

"BASIC TABLET WEAVING" BY "SARA"
http://www.duke.edu/~scg3/basictw.html

"HOW TO WARP YOUR FRAME LOOM" BY NIGEL HALL
http://www.hallnet.com/warp.html

THE WEAVE STUDY GROUP
http://www.hifiber.com/wsg.html

In 1995, a group of weavers on CompuServe formed a study group to work through "The Complete Book of Drafting for Handweavers" by Madelyn van der Hoogt. This page, organized by Deanna Johnson and Janis Saunders, details their progress.

Information on Looms

"HOW TO BUILD A FRAME LOOM" BY NIGEL HALL
http://www.hallnet.com/build.html

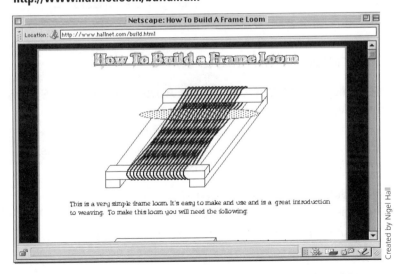

Created by Nigel Hall

"TOLI'S INEXPENSIVE INKLE/CARDWEAVING LOOM DESIGN" BY TIM MYERS FREEL
http://www.mtsu.edu/~kgregg/dmir/new/inkle/loom.html

LOOM CONSTRUCTION REFERENCES
FROM HALF WAY TREE LLC
http://www.halfwaytree.com/looms/

WARP-WEIGHTED LOOM INFORMATION,
FROM THE WOOL CAMP
http://www.dmv.com/~iceland/vefstadur/vefstadur.html

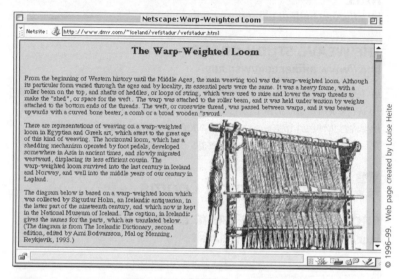

The Warp-Weighted Loom

From the beginning of Western history until the Middle Ages, the main weaving tool was the warp-weighted loom. Although its particular form varied through the ages and by locality, its essential parts were the same. It was a heavy frame, with a roller beam on the top, and shafts of heddles, or loops of string, which were used to raise and lower the warp threads to make the "shed", or space for the weft. The warp was attached to the roller beam, and it was held under tension by weights attached to the bottom ends of the threads. The weft, or crosswise thread, was passed between warps, and it was beaten upwards with a curved bone beater, a comb or a broad wooden "sword."

There are representations of weaving on a warp-weighted loom in Egyptian and Greek art, which attest to the great age of this kind of weaving. The horizontal loom, which has a shedding mechanism operated by foot pedals, developed somewhere in Asia in ancient times, and slowly migrated westward, displacing its less efficient cousin. The warp-weighted loom survived into the last century in Iceland and Norway, and well into the middle years of our century in Lapland.

The diagram below is based on a warp-weighted loom which was collected by Sigurdur Holm, an Icelandic antiquarian, in the latter part of the nineteenth century, and which now is kept in the National Museum of Iceland. The caption, in Icelandic, gives the names for the parts, which are translated below. (The diagram is from The Icelandic Dictionary, second edition, edited by Arni Bodvarsson, Mal og Menning, Reykjavik, 1993.)

© 1996–99. Web page created by Louise Heite

 Weaving Resources

RUTHE'S COLLECTION OF WEAVING RESOURCES
http://home.netinc.ca/~rstowe/weave.html

Ruthe Stowe offers a virtual library of links to weaving resources on the Net, including mailing lists. She offers a tips and tricks page, and info on the Cyber Dish Towel Exchange.

THE WEAVING LIST ARCHIVE
http://archives.his.com/weaving/

You can read past messages exchanged in the archives of the big mailing list discussion group for weavers.

TABLET WEAVING ARCHIVE
http://www.mtsu.edu/~kgregg/SCA/cards.html

Read the archives from the Tablet Weaving List.

C.W.'S NAVAJO WEAVING CORNER
http://www.uccs.edu/~cwetheri/NW/index.html

C. Wetherill's Navajo Weaving Corner

Alahane! Ha de sha? As far as I've been able to determine, this is one of only two pages on the Web by a weaver of Navajo textiles. (BTW: is Spider Woman responsible for the I-Net, too? eg...) Exhaustive searches are almost impossible since cyberspace is boundless, so please drop me a thread if you know of any other weavers out there with pages up. I've been getting several emails per month as of late - so it's good to know that Navajo weaving continues to have a strong interest out there. Keep writing - and weaving.

I've also been a researcher in this field and will refer you to my paper about "Astronomical Imagery in Navajo Weaving" for a consideration of that topic. (I'm sorry that the 17 slides used as illustrations are not available.)

This is a picture of my weaving teacher, Mary McKibben, next to her loom. She's been weaving in the traditional Navajo style since the age of six: "My mother would take out my small loom and set it up beside her large loom. I learned to weave sitting at her side... Weaving is a very spiritual thing... when I weave I think of my relatives and my old friends at school. My grandmother always used to say that your thoughts are woven into your rug... It's really nice to know some kind of artwork that gives you peace."

Created by Chris Wetherill

Chris Wetherill shares Navajo weaving information, photos, and links to other information on the Web.

LYNELLE'S WEAVING LINKS PAGE
http://members.aol.com/lynellevh/weaving.htm

This is a nice compilation of links, including galleries, guilds, and information on software.

ACADIAN TEXTILE TERMINOLOGY
http://netserver.huec.lsu.edu/acadian/att.html

Read selections from the Acadian Handicraft Project Papers, the exhibit catalog of Louisiana State Museum's L'Amour de Maman, and an interview with Audrey Bernard, noted weaver and collector of Acadian textiles and tools.

Find Out If Your Tartan Is Really a Tartan

"A pattern is not a tartan unless you can fold it diagonally so that the colors match," writes Dick Grune of Amsterdam. On his site he explains the mathematics in the patterning of tartans (**ftp://ftp.cs.vu.nl/pub/dick/tartan/0HowToCountATartan**).

STRUCTURAL DESIGN OF TEXTILES
http://char.txa.cornell.edu/zbs/webdocs/media/textile/structur.htm

Definitions of weaving terminology from Cornell University.

TABLET WEAVER'S RESOURCES
http://w3.thegroup.net/~janis/resources.html

Janis Saunders of the Weaver's Hand has compiled an extensive collection of links to information on the Web.

WEAVING AND CORDAGE
http://www.nativeweb.org/NativeTech/weave/index.html

Tara Prindle from Native American Technology and Art presents information on weaving and cordage.

SHUTTLE LINKS HOME PAGE
http://www.ghgcorp.com/stilgar/shuttlelinks/index.htm

ShuttleWorks, makers of software for weavers, offers a comprehensive list of links to weaving information on the Web.

 ## *Weaving Guilds*

HANDWEAVERS GUILD OF AMERICA
http://www.weavespindye.org/

The site offers membership information, Shuttle Spindle & Dyepot, the quarterly journal of HGA info, and a fabulous assortment of weaving-related Net links.

HGA GUILDS AND ORGANIZATIONS LIST
http://weavespindye.org/html/guildlnk.htm

The HGA offers a huge list of links to the Web pages and contact information of fiber, spinning, and weaving guilds throughout the world.

THE BEADWRANGLER WEAVERS GUILD LIST
http://www.beadwrangler.com/weaverslist.htm

Beadwrangler offers a list of weaver's guilds around the world.

Weaving Magazines

WEAVERS MAGAZINE ONLINE
http://www.xrx-inc.com/weavers/weavers/weavers.html

HANDWOVEN
http://www.interweave.com/iwpsite/handwoven/handwoven.html

Weaving Museums

WEAVING ART MUSEUM AND RESEARCH INSTITUTE
http://www.weavingartmuseum.org/

View pictures from the inaugural exhibition.

WEAVING AT THE GETTY MUSEUM
http://www.artsednet.getty.edu/ArtsEdNet/Index/Themes/weaving.html

Navajo blankets are discussed in this offering from the Getty Education Institute for the Arts.

RHODE ISLAND SCHOOL OF DESIGN
http://www.risd.edu/text/textalias.html

You can view a large gallery of student and faculty work in the textiles department.

THE BAUHAUS SCHOOL
http://www.cs.umb.edu/~alilley/bauhaus.html

Angela Lilleystone offers comprehensive links to Bauhaus art exhibits around the Web, plus many good essays including one on the role of women in the Bauhaus Weaving Workshop.

Weaving Discussions

You'll find weavers in the **Usenet** newsgroups **rec.crafts.textiles.yarn** and **rec.crafts.textiles.misc**.

You'll also find them in **CompuServe's** Fibercrafts forum (use the go word "fibercrafts" to get there). The forum also offers some terrific libraries of information and files for weavers.

 Weaving Bulletin Boards

WEAVING AT THE MINING COMPANY
http://weaving.miningco.com/

DELPHI'S TEXTILE ARTS FORUM WEAVING BOARD
http://www.delphi.com/textile/

WEAVER'S MAGAZINE'S WEFT TALK
http://205.164.216.225/scripts/webx.dll?wefTalk

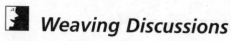 *Weaving Mailing Lists*

WEAVING
http://www.quilt.net/weaving.html

TABLET WEAVERS

E-mail tabletweaving-request@majordomo.net *with the single word message:* subscribe.

TAPESTRY

E-mail majordomo@ncn.com, *in the body of the message type* subscribe tapestry.

CARDS-L
http://www.mtsu.edu/~kregg/SCA/cards.html

SMALL LOOMS
http://www.xws.com/terispage/spindle.html

Visit Teri Pittman's page or e-mail loom@xws.com, *in the subject line, type* subscribe *or* subscribe digest.

Weaving Software

There are many, many software programs available for weavers, from simple shareware programs which you can use to graph designs to complex ones that interface with computerized looms. This list is by no means all-inclusive, but should be enough to get your shopping started.

WEAVEMAKER ONE
http://www.avlusa.com/TDS/SOFTWARE/WeaveMaker1.html
http://www.weavemaker.com/

From loom-maker AVL, WeaveMaker can be used to create designs for both treadle and dobby looms. Demos available for both Windows and Macs.

FIBERWORKS PCW
http://www3.sympatico.ca/fiberworks.pcw/

Download a demo of the drawdown software by Ingrid Boesel. A Windows version is available, a Mac version is forthcoming.

TURNSTYLER
http://www.hifiber.com/

Deanna M. Johnson created this PC program for card or tablet weaving. You can download a demo.

WEAVEIT
http://www.weaveit.com/

Download a demo of this Windows design software from Canyon Art Co. that will let you create threading, treadling, and tie-up draft, and Weavelt will display the drawdown.

free Stuff for Fiber and Fabric Dyers

Every stitcher reaches a point in his or her career when Rit Dye just doesn't make it any longer. Maybe you want to "antique" a swatch of lace by tea-dyeing it. Or perhaps you want to color that ho-hum dog fur you've just spinned. Whether you're looking for how-tos on batiking or dyeing with Kool-Aid, dyeing in a tub in the backyard or in the microwave, you'll find them on the Web.

 *For Those Dyeing to Get Started*

🛒 COFFEE DYE RECIPE FOR LACES AND TRIM
http://www.laboursoflove.com/p1302.htm

Labours Of Love offers a tutorial for antiqueing trim with coffee.

DYEING RECIPES AND ADVICE FROM *RUG HOOKING* MAGAZINE:

Rug Hooking *magazine offers terrific articles and recipes from their archives that will have you dyeing wool with onion skins, dyeing in an electric fry pan, and performing the art of "salt shaker dyeing." Some include:*

"ADVENTURES IN DYEING: EXPERIENCED DYERS SHARE THEIR TECHNIQUES"
http://www.rughookingonline.com/dyeing/adventures.html

"HANGING AROUND WAITING TO DYE: THE SECRETS OF COAT HANGER DYEING" BY JANE MCGOWN FLYNN
http://www.rughookingonline.com/waiting/hanger.html

"BASIC JAR DYEING INSTRUCTIONS" BY MARYANNE LINCOLN
http://www.rughookingonline.com/basic/jardye.html

"RECIPES FROM THE DYE KITCHEN"
BY MARYANNE LINCOLN
http://www.rughookingonline.com/archives.html

"DYEING NEEDLEPOINT THREADS"
http://needlepoint.miningco.com/library/weekly/aa062698.htm

Janet Perry at The Mining Co.'s Needlepoint site is full of good advice on dyeing threads with Kool-Aid, Jell-O, tea, and other kitchen supplies. Good article if you've never dyed before.

KNITNET'S ADVICE ON DYEING FIBERS
http://www.woolworks.org/dyeing.html

Want to dye mohair with Kool-Aid? Emily Way offers a collection of messages gleaned from the KnitNet mailing list, and also the Weaver's list on dyeing fibers.

PUGGLE'S FIBER WORLD DYEING PAGE
http://members.aol.com/hostpuggle/dyepg.html

This page should really be subtitled "Anything Your Husband Can Eat Out of You Can Dye In." Learn how to dye fabric and fiber in jars, casserole dishes, mugs, and more.

🛒 LOIS CARON'S GUIDE TO HAND-DYED
THREAD, THE CARON COLLECTION
http://www.caron-net.com/featurefiles/featapr.html

Caron of the world-famous thread-maker of the same name divulges details on how Caron embroidery floss is dyed, including the types of dye used, how different types of floss reacts with different dyes, and gives the lowdown on dyelots, over-dying, mordanting, and more.

FABRIC DYEING FAQ
http://www.masterstech-home.com/The_Sewing_Room/Articles/FabricDyingFAQ.html

Colleen at Master's Tech offers a mini-tutorial on dyeing.

ALL ABOUT HAND DYEING ON FABRIC
http://www.flash.net/~pburch/dyeing.html

Paula Burch shares all sorts of information on dyeing, including information on batik and tie-dyeing.

JACQUARD PRODUCTS HOME PAGE
http://www.jacquardproducts.com

Makers of Gloria's favorite fabric paint, this site includes instructions on techniques such as silk painting, Procion dyeing, chemical resists, discharge pastes, and scrunch dyeing.

PAINTING FABRICS
http://www.patchwords.com/ofeatures/fabpaint.html

The quilting Web site Patch Words tells you what you need to know to get started.

QUILTNET DISCHARGE DYEING FAQ
http://quilt.com/FAQS/DischargeDyeingFAQ.html

This is a compilation of messages posted to the discussion group Quiltnet. It includes a color wheel and tips on creating a suede-like look in fabrics.

"BASIC INSTRUCTIONS FOR WORKING WITH REACTIVE AND WASHFAST ACID DYES" BY PAT WILLIAMS
http://164.76.4.21/faculty/williams/basicdyeinstr.html

Pat Williams offers some great dyeing recipes.

Now Find Out What's In Your Hair Dye

We've talked about dyes for fiber, fabric, ribbon, and thread. But what about the dye you use in your hair? Find out what you're putting on your head at **Paula Begoun's Cosmetics Cop (http://www.cosmeticscop .com).** Be sure to read her answers to visitors' questions.

🛒 STRAW INTO GOLD
DYE INFORMATION AND RECIPES
http://www.straw.com/sig/sigmenu1.html

Susan Druding supplies great tutorials on dyeing wool, acid dyeing, simplified Procion dyeing, the history of dyeing, and lots more. (You can trust Susan's advice. This lady knows everything about dyeing.)

🛒 CARYL FALLERT'S FABRIC DYEING
AND PAINTING FAQ
http://www.bryerpatch.com/faq/dyeing.htm

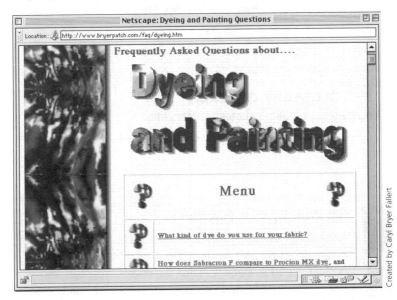

Created by Caryl Bryer Fallert

Quilt artist Fallert answers questions like "Do you dye in the washing machine or do you stand there and stir?"

BASIC DYEING
http://www.patchwords.com/ofeatures/dyeing.html

DYEING TECHNIQUES AND DISCUSSION
http://www.pbm.com/~lindahl/rialto/dyeing-msg.html

DYEING AND PAINTING LEATHER
http://www.pbm.com/~lindahl/rialto//leather-dyeing-msg.html

Mark Harris offers a collection of information on dyeing that he's collected from his "readings on various computer networks."

 ## "FABRIC DYEING IN THE MICROWAVE" FROM THE COTTON CLUB
http://www.cottonclub.com/dyeing.htm

The Cotton Club offers easy-to-follow instructions.

 ## DHARMA TRADING CO.
http://www.dharmatrading.com/vat_dye.html

Dharma Trading Co. provides directions for many dyeing techniques, from the "soda soak method" to the "cold batch method," plus advice on wool and silk dyeing.

 ## GLOSSARY OF TERMS
http://www.prochemical.com/glossary.htm

The folks at Pro Chemical & Dye define everything from Acetic Acid 56% to Wool Assistant SBS.

Chat With Dyers in FiberNet

Wondering how to dye that sheep's fleece you just bought on eBay? Join the audacious mailing list discussion FiberNet. Head to page 171 for directions. You can also search archives of FiberNet's past messages by heading to **Lois Baker's FiberLink** **(http://www.benefitslink.com/knit/fibernet /digests.shtml)**. Type a search term like "dyeing" or "fleece" and click Search. FiberNet will present a long list of archives. Click on one and after the message page loads, use your browser's search feature (Edit/Find) to search the big message list for the same word.

Exotic and Advanced Dyeing How-Tos

PAINT AND DYEING AT THE UNIVERSITY OF ALASKA, FAIRBANKS THEATRICAL COSTUME SHOP
http://costumes.org/pages/dyeing.htm

This site is wild! It includes pictures showing how UAF costumers painted tuxedos with leopard patterns for the prom scene in Grease *and outfit the entire cast of* Comedy of Errors *without sewing a stitch—they painted all the costumes. The pictures and dyeing stories here are mind-boggling. You'll want to run up to Alaska and join this mad creativity.*

CAROL TODD'S DYE PLANT OF THE MONTH
http://www.slonet.org/~crowland/PlantoftheMonth.html

This is a cool site! Carol's Natural Dyeing Web site tells you how to dye fibers and fabrics with things in your backyard like crabapple and honeysuckle leaves.

THE EDMONTON (CANADA) WEAVERS GUILD DYEING WITH KOOL-AID RECIPE
http://www.freenet.edmonton.ab.ca/weavers/dye.html

© 1999 Tara Maginnis

KATHRYN OF THE HILLS' DYE BOOK
http://www.cobweb.net/~ryn/dyebook.html

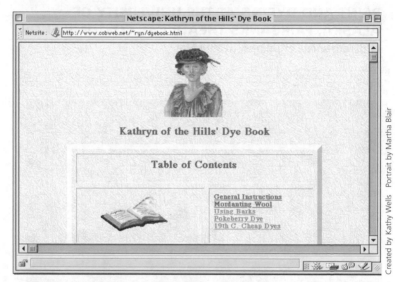

Kathryn Wells explains mordanting wool, how to use pokeberry dye, and more.

HAND MARBLING FOR QUILTERS, BY JANET WICKEL
http://www.UserHome.com/quilting/marble.html

"COLOR THEORY AS IT RELATES TO DYEING" BY JAMIESON FORSYTH
http://www.delphi.com/textile/98/dye-1.html

🛒 PROCION MX DYEING INSTRUCTIONS FROM G&S DYE
http://www.interlog.com/~gsdye/ProcionMX.html

G&S offers instructions for immersion dyeing, batik, and direct application tie-dye.

🛒 TIE-DYE INSTRUCTIONS FROM BEST DYE
http://www.bestdye.com/dye.htm

🛒 JOHN MARSHALL'S NATURAL DYES ON NATURAL FABRICS
http://www.johnmarshall.to/PageOne.html

Created by John Marshall to further interest and knowledge in Japanese textile arts. © John Marshall

Learn about Katazome, a form of paste resist surface design. John's site includes extensive Japanese dye and stenciling how-tos.

🛒 MENDEL'S TIE DYEING
http://www.mendels.com/tiedye.html

Groovy man! Mendel's FarOut Fabrics explains how-to tie-dye fabric.

"METHODS OF DISCHARGING DYE" BY PAT WILLIAMS
http://www.art.acad.emich.edu/faculty/williams/specialdyeinstr.html#discharge

Pat explains several methods of removing color from previously dyed textiles.

🛒 THE RIT DYE CUSTOM COLOR RECIPE CHART
http://members.aol.com/violinart1/ritdye.html

The Basket Class and Rit offer recipes for creating the color you want with Rit Dyes.

"DYEING WITH INDIGO"
BY M. JOAN LINTAULT AND JOANNA JOHNSON
http://www.lintault.com/indigodye/

Organized by Joanna Johnson and Brice Gustin.
© 1999 Created by M. Joan Lintault

THE WOAD PAGE
http://www.net-link.net/~rowan/woad.html
"Rowan" explains how to use woad, a plant which produces a blue dye.

 *Dyeing Safety Advice*

QUILTNET FABRIC DYEING SAFETY FAQ
http://quilt.com/FAQS/DyeSafetyFaq.html

STUDIO SAFETY AND GUIDELINES
FROM PRO CHEMICAL & DYE
http://www.prochemical.com/studio.htm

"COSTUME CRAFTS AT 50 BELOW: THE FAIRBANKS NON-TOXIC CRAFTS COOKBOOK"
http://costumes.org/pages/cookbook.htm

Tara Maginnis, Ph.D. of the University of Alaska, Fairbanks costume department offers a "cookbook" of suggestions on how to dye fabric using non-toxic rather than toxic dyes and substances. For example, instead of marbling fabric with oil paint thinned with turpentine she suggests water-thinned Neopaque on a surface of carrageenan. She offers a source list and suggested readings.

Indispensable Dyeing Discussions

DYERS LIST SEARCHABLE ARCHIVE
http://www2.art.acad.emich.edu/lists/dyerslist/search.html

Should you decide to plunge into the dye pot consider joining the Dyers e-mail list, hosted by Pat Williams of the art department of Eastern Michigan University (see URL on page 168) or search the archive for information on immersion dyeing and the surface application of synthetic dyes, textile pigments, and other chemicals on fabric and fiber.

NATURAL DYES MAILING LIST & ARCHIVES
http://www47.pair.com/lindo/dyelist.htm
or head to OneList at http://www.onelist.com

Mara Riley's is for those interested in using plants and "gentle" homemade dyes.

SPINNERS IN DELPHI'S TEXTILE ARTS FORUM
http://www.delphi.com/textile

Click on Message Boards and scroll down to Spinning & Fibers to get to the bulletin board-style discussion area.

DYERS E-MAIL LIST
http://www.art.acad.emich.edu/lists/dyerslist/dyerslist.html

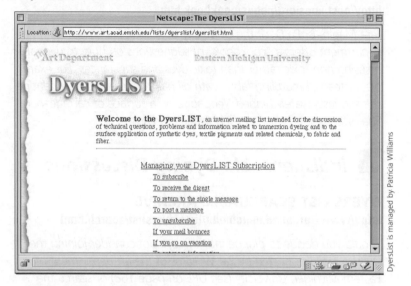

DyersList is managed by Patricia Williams

BATIK-ML
http://www.neosoft.com/internet/paml/groups.B/batik-ml.html

To subscribe to this discussion for batik dyers run by Albert Buys e-mail majordomo@bear-buys.com *with* subscribe batik-ml *as the message. You can read archives of past messages at* http://206.241.12.9/archives/batik-ml.html.

SPINNING & DYEING AT THE MINING CO.
http://spinning.miningco.com/

Rosemary Brock runs a wonderful forum with feature articles, a bulletin board, and links to all the best spots on the Web for those interested in dyeing wool. She offers an especially good list of links for those interested in natural dyeing with topics like dyeing with mushrooms and an exploration of Renaissance dyes.